REVISE BTEC FIRST

Business

Unit 2 Finance for Business

Unit 9 Principles of Marketing

REVISION WORKBOOK

Series Consultant: Harry Smith   Authors: Carol Carysforth and Mike Neild

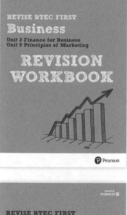

THE REVISE BTEC SERIES

BTEC First in Business Revision Workbook   9781446906699

BTEC First in Business Revision Guide   9781446906682

This Workbook is designed to complement your classroom and home learning, and to help prepare you for the exam. It does not include all the content and skills needed for the complete course. It is designed to work in combination with Pearson's main BTEC First series.

For the full range of Pearson revision titles across KS2, KS3, GCSE, Functional Skills, AS/A Level and BTEC visit:
www.pearsonschools.co.uk/revise

Published by Pearson Education Limited, Edinburgh Gate, Harlow, Essex, CM20 2JE.

www.pearsonschoolsandfecolleges.co.uk

Copies of official specifications for all Pearson qualifications may be found on the website: www.edexcel.com

Text © Pearson Education Limited 2014
Typeset by Tech-Set Ltd, Gateshead
Original illustrations © Pearson Education Limited
Cover photo/illustration by Miriam Sturdee

The rights of Carol Carysforth and Mike Neild to be identified as authors of this work has been asserted by them in accordance with the Copyright, Designs and Patents Act 1988.

First published 2014

19 18 17
10 9 8 7 6 5 4 3 2

British Library Cataloguing in Publication Data
A catalogue record for this book is available from the British Library

ISBN 978 1 4469 0669 9

Printed in Slovakia by Neografia

Acknowledgements

The publisher would like to thank the following for their kind permission to reproduce their photographs:
(Key: b-bottom; c-centre; l-left; r-right; t-top)

DK Images: Dave King 21tl; **Fotolia.com:** asaijdler 28bl, bit24 21bl, Christopher Dodge 28br, Ingus Evertovskis 21tr; **Veer / Corbis:** Alliance 64, CaptureLight 1, Corepics 3, haveseen 5, Monkey Business images 42, Mykola Lunov 14, naumoid 49, photosoup 28tc, stillfx 7, Vladimir Koletic 28tl
All other images © Pearson Education

Picture Research by: Susie Prescott

Every effort has been made to trace the copyright holders and we apologise in advance for any unintentional omissions. We would be pleased to insert the appropriate acknowledgement in any subsequent edition of this publication.

A note from the publisher

In order to ensure that this resource offers high-quality support for the associated BTEC qualification, it has been through a review process by the awarding body to confirm that it fully covers the teaching and learning content of the specification or part of a specification at which it is aimed, and demonstrates an appropriate balance between the development of subject skills, knowledge and understanding, in addition to preparation for assessment.

While the publishers have made every attempt to ensure that advice on the qualification and its assessment is accurate, the official specification and associated assessment guidance materials are the only authoritative source of information and should always be referred to for definitive guidance.

BTEC examiners have not contributed to any sections in this resource relevant to examination papers for which they have responsibility.

No material from an endorsed book will be used verbatim in any assessment set by BTEC.

Endorsement of a book does not mean that the book is required to achieve this BTEC qualification, nor does it mean that it is the only suitable material available to support the qualification, and any resource lists produced by the awarding body shall include this and other appropriate resources.

Contents

This book covers the externally assessed units in the BTEC Level 1/Level 2 First in Business qualification.

Unit 2 Finance for Business
Learning aim A
1 Start-up costs
2 Operating (running) costs
3 Fixed and variable costs
4 Calculating total costs
5 Sources of revenue
6 Calculating revenue
7 Types of expenditure
8 Understanding and calculating profit or loss

Learning aim B
9 Break-even charts
10 Interpreting break-even charts
11 Using the breakeven formula to calculate the break-even point
12 The value of breakeven analysis and the risks of ignoring it
13 The effect of changes on the break-even point
14 The purpose of budgeting
15 Budgeting and budgetary control
16 Cash flow forecasting
17 Calculating net inflows/outflows
18 Impact of timings on cash flow
19 The benefits of using a cash flow forecast and the risks of not doing it
20 Completing and analysing cash flow forecasts

Learning aim C
21 Cost of sales
22 Gross profit
23 The impact of positive and negative gross profit
24 Net profit
25 The impact of positive and negative net profit
26 Financial statements
27 Income statement (profit and loss account)
28 Assets, liabilities and working capital
29 The statement of financial position (balance sheet)
30 Completing a statement of financial position (balance sheet)
31 Increasing profits and analysing an income statement (profit and loss account)
32 Analysing a statement of financial position (balance sheet) for a small business
33 Exam skills 1
34 Exam skills 2
35 Exam skills 3

Unit 9 Principles of Marketing
Learning aim A
36 Defining marketing and its importance to business
37 How businesses use marketing
38 Marketing, corporate objectives and SMART objectives
39 B2B and B2C markets
40 Other types of markets
41 Business models
42 Business orientation and choice of business model
43 Branding – its importance and dimensions
44 The benefits of building brands

Learning aim B
45 Market research – types and sources of data
46 The uses of data to support marketing activity
47 The uses of internal and external data and situational analysis
48 The purpose of market research and analysis
49 Interpreting key market research findings
50 PESTLE analysis

Learning aim C
51 The marketing mix – an overview
52 Product differentiation
53 Product life cycle
54 Product portfolios
55 Pricing strategies
56 Elasticity of demand
57 Place – distribution channels
58 Place – business location
59 The promotional mix, budget and channels
60 Viral marketing and guerrilla advertising
61 Consistency and the marketing mix
62 Ebusiness and ecommerce
63 Influences on the marketing mix
64 Evaluating the effectiveness of the marketing mix
65 Exam skills 1
66 Exam skills 2
67 Exam skills 3

68 **Unit 2: Practice assessment test**

74 **Unit 9: Practice assessment test**

79 **Answers**

 Guided These questions provide part of a model answer to help you get started.

A bit of small print

Pearson publishes Sample Assessment Material and the Specification on its website. That is the official content, and this book should be used in conjunction with it. The questions in this book have been written to help you practise what you have learned in your revision. Remember: the real test questions may not look like this.

Start-up costs

1

> Which **two** of the following are start-up costs for a mobile car valeting business?
> Put a cross in the box next to the correct ones.   **(2 marks)**

A ☐ Petrol for the van

B ☐ A pressure washer

C ☐ Car wash shampoo

D ☐ Overalls for the staff

E ☐ Paper for customer receipts

> Make sure you are clear about the number of items you must identify **and** the key term you are being asked about.

▷ Guided ▷   **2** Tom is setting up a business as a boarding kennels. He will look after dogs while the owners are away on holiday. He has found a barn that he can rent. It will need fitting out with secure kennels and runs for the dogs.

> For questions like this, think carefully about the business **context** before you answer. What type of money would be spent to start this type of business?

> Identify **three** start-up costs he may have.   **(3 marks)**

1   Feeding bowls/dog leads and other dog care items

2   ....

....

3   ....

....

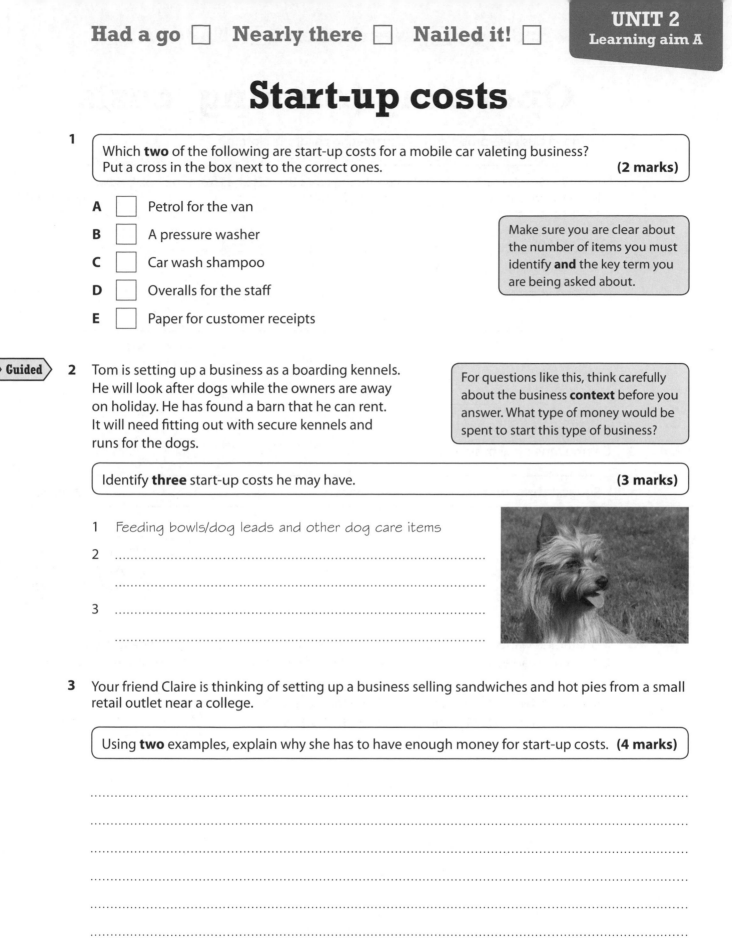

3 Your friend Claire is thinking of setting up a business selling sandwiches and hot pies from a small retail outlet near a college.

> Using **two** examples, explain why she has to have enough money for start-up costs.   **(4 marks)**

....

....

....

....

....

....

....

....

Operating (running) costs

1 Lisa runs a business producing and marketing children's clothing.

> Identify **two** start-up costs and **two** running costs that Lisa has from the box below. Place the words in the correct column of the table. **(2 marks)**

Start-up costs	Running costs

> Shelves/rails for storing stock   Sewing machine
>
> Thread   Electricity

Guided   **2** George runs a taxi business.

> Suggest **three** running costs he might have. **(3 marks)**

1   Petrol/diesel

2   ....

3   ....

> Think about the costs involved in running a car before you answer.

3 Mohammed wants to start a business selling second-hand books, computer games, DVDs and CDs from a market stall. He does not know the difference between start-up and running costs.

> **(a)** Which **two** of the following would be examples of his running costs?
> Put a cross in the box next to the correct statement. **(2 marks)**

A ☐ Buying items to resell

B ☐ Paying to have a market pitch for a year

C ☐ Buying a safe to keep cash overnight

D ☐ Paying his brother to help out on a Saturday

E ☐ Paying for boxes to display his stock

> **(b)** Outline what is meant by the term 'running costs'. **(1 mark)**

....

....

Fixed and variable costs

1   Anita runs a business making small wooden toys, such as trains and boats. She uses a workshop which she bought with a bank loan, and employs a friend to help out on a part-time basis when she is busy.

> **(a)** Suggest **four** fixed costs that Anita might pay.   **(4 marks)**

1 ....

2 ....

3 ....

4 ....

> Make sure you are clear about the term you are being asked about. Here you are being asked to identify **fixed** costs.

> **(b)** Now suggest **two** variable costs that she might have.   **(2 marks)**

1 ....

2 ....

Guided   2

> Complete the following sentences using the words in the box below.   **(2 marks)**

(a) Rent is usually a fixed cost because it does not .... regardless of the level of activity or the number of items made and sold.

(b) Postage and packing costs are often variable costs because the cost .... with the level of activity or as more items are made, sold and despatched.

change	variable	decreases
fixed	increases	varies

Calculating total costs

1   **(a)** Complete the following formula to show how the variable cost figure is calculated using **one** of the choices from the box below.   **(1 mark)**

Variable costs = ... × Number of units produced

Cost of one unit	Sales revenue
Fixed costs	Cost of ten units

(b) If one unit costs £5 and 50 units are produced, calculate the total variable cost.   **(1 mark)**

....

Guided

2   Complete the formula below for total costs by choosing the correct words and inserting them in the right place.   **(1 mark)**

Start-up costs	Fixed costs	Running costs	Variable costs

Total costs = ... + Variable costs

3   A business has the following monthly costs.

Fixed costs	£400
Variable costs	£10 per item

(a) What are the variable costs if they make 100 items?   **(1 mark)**

....

(b) What is the fixed cost if they make 100 items?   **(1 mark)**

> Think about the definition of fixed costs before you answer this question and the next!

....

(c) What are their total costs if they increase production to 200 items a month?   **(1 mark)**

....

Sources of revenue

Guided

1 Simon has a cycle shop. He sells bikes and also carries out repairs. The shop is on a corner so it has a large side wall which people can see as they walk by. He rents this out for advertising space to local companies. He has a spare room upstairs which he rents out to a small printing business. He also puts any surplus cash into a savings account each week.

> Identify **four** sources of income for Simon's business.   **(4 marks)**

1   Sales revenue from selling bikes | Remember that revenue and income mean the same thing. |

2 ....

3 ....

4 ....

2 Energy Fitness is a fitness centre in a small town. Its main income comes from subscription fees from members. The manager, Dave, is looking at other ways to make money for the centre.

> Suggest **two** other possible sources of income from customers.   **(2 marks)**

1 ....

2 ....

3 Gareth's main source of income at the garden centre is from selling plants. He is now listing his other sources of income.

> Which **two** of the following items should be on his list? Put a cross in the box next to the two correct items.   **(2 marks)**

A ☐ Taking on casual staff

B ☐ Selling wild bird food

C ☐ Giving staff discounts

D ☐ Offering plant food and weedkiller for sale

E ☐ Buying plants to sell

Calculating revenue

1   Give the formula for calculating revenue by choosing the correct words and inserting them in the right place. **(1 mark)**

| Fixed costs | Price per unit | Start-up costs |
| Variable costs | Number of sales | Total costs |

> Remember you will be calculating money received with this formula.

Revenue = ... × ....

2   In a month, a business making computer desks sells 300 desks. The price of each desk is £30.

(a) What is their total revenue per month? **(1 mark)**

....

(b) If they sell the same number every month, what is their total annual revenue? **(1 mark)**

....

....

> Even if you can do these calculations in your head, use a calculator to check you are correct.

> **Guided**

3   Max has a van and sells ice lollies and candy floss at fairgrounds. The ice lollies sell for £1.00 and sticks of candy floss for £1.50. Yesterday Max sold 200 ice lollies and 300 bags of candy floss.

What is his total revenue? **(2 marks)**

200 x £1.00 = ...

.... x £...................... = ...

> Always look for the key term in a question. Here it is **total revenue**.

Total revenue = £...................... + £...................... = £......................

Types of expenditure

1 Kate runs a gift shop called 'Candy and Cards'.

Which **two** of these items are examples of her expenditure?
Put a cross in the box next to the two correct statements.   **(2 marks)**

A ☐ Buying cards to sell

B ☐ Sale of sweets

C ☐ Wages for an assistant

D ☐ Interest on money in a savings account

E ☐ A bank loan for an extension

2 Tom runs a key cutting business from a kiosk in the town centre.

Suggest **two** items of expenditure that he will have.   **(2 marks)**

1 ....

2 ....

Guided   **3** Jasper has heard the term 'overheads' being used but does not know what this means.

Outline what this means for him.   **(1 mark)**

Overheads are the everyday .... of a business.

> When you are asked to outline something, you should give a short definition.

7

Understanding and calculating profit or loss

1 Choose **one** of the words from the box below to complete the formula for calculating profit. **(1 mark)**

Profit = ... – Expenditure

Overheads	Fixed costs	Revenue
Total costs	Outflows	Variable costs

> If you are not sure of the answer, first try to find words that are connected to something else. For example, outflows are linked to cash flow, so you know that is not the right answer.

2 Last month Ken's business had an income from sales of £30,000 and expenditure of £25,000.

Use the formula to calculate his profit/loss figure.
Show whether this is a positive figure (a profit) or a negative figure (a loss). **(1 mark)**

....

....

> **Guided**

3 A business wants to increase its profits. Describe how it can do this. **(4 marks)**

It can increase revenue. This means ....

....

.... It can reduce

> Give a short description of a few sentences without going into detail.

....

....

These actions will help it to increase profits because revenue and ....

are both used to calculate profit. The greater the revenue received and the lower the

...., the higher the .... that is left.

Break-even charts

> **Guided** **1** | State the purpose of a break-even chart. **(1 mark)**

The purpose of a break-even chart is to demonstrate how many units

have to be ....

....

....

....

> This question focuses on why a break-even chart is created. Get straight to the point with your answer.

2 | Label the line on the chart with the correct term. Write in the box next to that line. **(1 mark)**

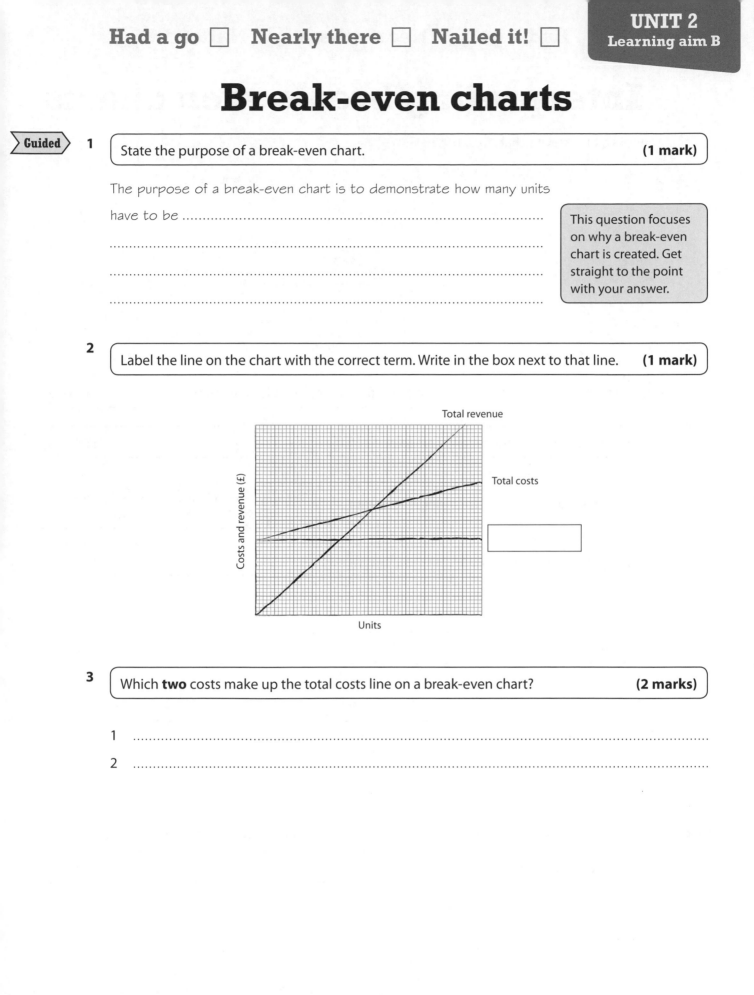

3 | Which **two** costs make up the total costs line on a break-even chart? **(2 marks)**

1 ....

2 ....

Interpreting break-even charts

Here is a break-even chart for a business.

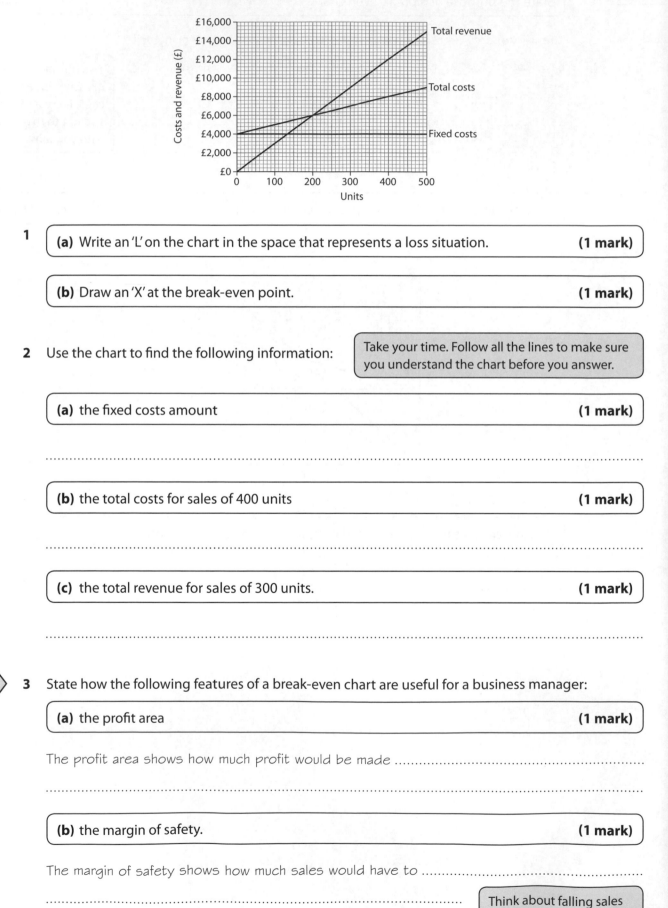

1

(a) Write an 'L' on the chart in the space that represents a loss situation. **(1 mark)**

(b) Draw an 'X' at the break-even point. **(1 mark)**

2   Use the chart to find the following information:

> Take your time. Follow all the lines to make sure you understand the chart before you answer.

(a) the fixed costs amount **(1 mark)**

....

(b) the total costs for sales of 400 units **(1 mark)**

....

(c) the total revenue for sales of 300 units. **(1 mark)**

....

Guided   3   State how the following features of a break-even chart are useful for a business manager:

(a) the profit area **(1 mark)**

The profit area shows how much profit would be made ....

....

(b) the margin of safety. **(1 mark)**

The margin of safety shows how much sales would have to ....

....

> Think about falling sales and the break-even point.

Using the breakeven formula to calculate the break-even point

Guided

1   A business manufactures three types of furniture in three different factories. The table shows their predicted figures for the next year for each item.

> Complete the table by using the breakeven formula to calculate the break-even point of each item.   **(3 marks)**

The formula is:

> In the test you should use the calculator function for questions like these. Start by calculating the bottom line answer first. Then divide this into the fixed costs.

$$\text{Break-even point} = \frac{\text{Fixed costs}}{\text{Selling price per unit} - \text{Variable cost per unit}}$$

$$\text{Item } 1 = \frac{1,000}{50 - 30} = 50$$

Furniture items	Fixed costs (£)	Selling price per unit (£)	Variable cost per unit (£)	Break-even point
Item 1	1,000	50	30	50
Item 2	300	25	10	
Item 3	7,000	100	30	

2   Supergates is a business that is planning to make stair gates to keep young children safe.

Imran, the business owner, wants to know how many stair gates he needs to make. He therefore needs to work out how many he needs to sell to break even. He writes down some financial information for a typical week.

     Fixed costs £1,500   Selling price per unit £35   Variable costs per unit £20

> **(a)** Use this information to calculate the number of stair gates he will need to sell each week to begin to make a profit.   **(1 mark)**

....

Imran has discovered that a competitor is selling stair gates for £30 and he thinks that he may have to match this price.

> **(b)** Calculate his new break-even point.   **(1 mark)**

....

The value of breakeven analysis and the risks of ignoring it

1

Which **two** of these are advantages of using breakeven analysis? Put a cross in the box next to the correct statements.

(2 marks)

A ☐ The total costs are calculated

B ☐ The effect of competitors' selling prices can be seen

C ☐ The effect of changes in raw material prices can be assessed

D ☐ The reasons for changes in consumer demand are known

E ☐ The margin of safety is unknown

Guided

2 Your friend, Nadia, runs a small business making clothes for young girls. She complains to you that, although she has lots of orders, she is still losing money.

Discuss how using breakeven analysis could help Nadia ensure her business is successful.

(8 marks)

Here is a plan you could use for your answer:
- State the purpose of breakeven analysis. Relate this to Nadia's business and the problems she may be having.
- Explain how it can help her business – give three or four actions she can take using the information from breakeven analysis.
- Explain how each action will help to ensure Nadia's future success – what else will she be able to go on to do?

....

....

....

....

....

....

....

....

....

....

....

....

....

The effect of changes on the break-even point

1 Outline what would happen to the break-even point if each of these events occurs. **(3 marks)**

> You do not need to give detailed explanations to answer this type of question.

A The variable costs figure falls.

....

....

> You may find it helpful to sketch a break-even chart to work out these answers.

B The selling price increases.

....

....

C The fixed costs figure increases.

....

....

Guided **2** Give **two** reasons why a business would want to carry out a breakeven analysis every three months. **(2 marks)**

1 Sales could fall. The business may want to lower the price for a short time to

boost sales.

> Remember things are always changing in business!

2 ....

3 Martin has a sandwich shop. The supplier of his bread has recently increased his costs. At the same time, the rent on Martin's shop has increased.

(a) What effect will these increases have on Martin's break-even point? **(1 mark)**

....

(b) Suggest **two** actions he could take to improve his business' prospects. **(2 marks)**

1 ....

2 ....

The purpose of budgeting

1   Holly has a busy alterations and accessories business and is setting her first budget.

> Identify the budget to which she should allocate each of the following items. Place each item in the correct column in the table.   **(2 marks)**

| Staff wages | Electricity charges |
| Money from alterations | Income from fashion accessories |

Revenue budget	Expenditure budget

▷ **Guided** ▷ 2

> Outline the purpose of setting a revenue budget.   **(1 mark)**

The purpose of setting a revenue budget is to set .... for income from

.... This provides a focus for everyone involved in .... in the business.

3

> Explain **one** benefit of setting an expenditure budget.   **(2 marks)**

....

....

....

....

> Write two sentences. Focus on the importance of keeping expenditure to set limits.

Budgeting and budgetary control

Guided **1**

> Which **one** of the following best describes the purpose of budgetary control?
> Put a cross in the box next to the correct answer. **(1 mark)**

A ☐ To enable staff to spend more money on important items

B ☐ To ensure performance is checked against the agreed plan

~~**C** ☐ To reward staff who spend very little~~

> This answer might seem like a good idea but how would this work in practice? Imagine this is your business and decide which would be the best option.

D ☐ To give bonuses to staff who spend exactly the right amount

2

> Choose the correct phrase from the box below to complete the sentence on budgetary control. **(1 mark)**

Allowing an overspend in budgets, because of a lack of budgetary control, means that the business could be ....

| making a profit | breaking even | increasing sales revenue | making a loss |

3 A food production company operates a strict budgetary control system. The table below shows the planned (budgeted) spending and actual spending for three departments.

> Identify which department you would be concerned about. State the reason for your choice. **(2 marks)**

Department	Budgeted expenditure (£)	Actual expenditure (£)
A	3,000	3,100
B	4,500	5,500
C	6,000	5,950

....

....

Cash flow forecasting

1 Outline the purpose of a cash flow forecast. **(2 marks)**

....

....

2 A cash flow shows cash inflows and outflows. For each item put a cross in the correct box to show whether it is an inflow or an outflow. **(2 marks)**

	Inflow	Outflow
Purchase of raw materials	☐	☐
Interest on savings account	☐	☐
Insurance	☐	☐
Sales revenue	☐	☐

> The first two letters of these words are 'in' and 'out'. That should tell you whether you are looking at money coming into the business or money going out.

Guided

3 **(a)** Identify the most important item of information shown on a cash flow forecast. **(1 mark)**

The level of .... in the business.

(b) Explain **one** reason why a business owner needs to know this information. **(2 marks)**

....

....

....

> Write two sentences. Remember that this is a forecast.

Calculating net inflows/outflows

Guided **1** Anna is about to calculate her cash flow forecast.

> Which **one** of the following shows the information she needs to calculate net cash flow this month? **(1 mark)**

A ☐ Total inflows, total outflows and opening bank balance

B ☐ Total inflows, total outflows and closing bank balance

~~**C** ☐ Total outflows, opening balance, variable costs~~

~~**D** ☐ Total inflows, closing balance, total costs~~

> Costs are nothing to do with cash flow. Knowing that should help you to answer this question.

2 At the start of the year, Alec started his business with £3,000 in the bank.

> **(a)** During the month his net inflow was £2,000. Calculate his closing balance. **(1 mark)**

....

In February his inflows were £2,000 and his payments were £3,000.

> **(b)** What was his net cash flow for that month? **(1 mark)**

....

....

> Remember net cash flow can be positive or negative.

3 A business is preparing its cash flow forecast for June.

> Complete the figures in the cash flow forecast to show the net inflow/outflow and the closing balance. **(2 marks)**

	June (£)
Total receipts	£60,000
Total payments	£50,000
Net inflow/outflow	
Opening balance	£13,000
Closing balance	

Impact of timings on cash flow

1   Explain the difference between a cash transaction and a credit transaction.   **(2 marks)**

....

....

> **Guided**

2   Sophie supplies interior design shops with cushions she makes. Some are slow to pay their bills and this gives her a cash flow problem.

(a) Identify **two** ways she can try to improve the timing of these inflows.   **(2 marks)**

1   Offering discounts for prompt payments.

2   ....

Sophie thinks she could delay payments to her own suppliers.

(b) Explain **one** benefit and **one** drawback of this plan.   **(4 marks)**

....

....

....

....

| State one positive and one negative effect on her cash flow if she takes this action and then explain how it could affect her reputation and relationships with suppliers. |

3   The chart below shows the net cash flow for two businesses. One business is a sweet shop in the town centre and the other is an ice-cream van.

	Jan	Feb	Mar	April	May	June	July	Aug	Sept	Oct	Nov	Dec
Business A	£600	£600	£500	£650	£600	£400	£300	£400	£650	£600	£600	£400
Business B	£100	£100	£90	£150	£150	£450	£700	£650	£300	£200	£150	£70

(a) Identify which business is the ice-cream van.   **(1 mark)**

....

(b) Explain which business is likely to have the most problems with timings on cash flow.   **(2 marks)**

| This question requires you to give a reason for your choice. Link your answer to the businesses shown. |

....

....

(c) Give **one** action Business B could take to improve its cashflow in the winter months.
(1 mark)

....

The benefits of using a cash flow forecast and the risks of not doing it

1 Marcus has an airport transfer business. He has a minibus for families and an expensive saloon car for business clients.

> Give **two** reasons why a strong cash flow is important to Marcus. **(2 marks)**

1 ....

2 ....

> Think about why Marcus may need money quickly to pay a bill.

2 Families pay Marcus immediately but local businesses want an account so that they can pay monthly. Local businesses are important to Marcus because they use his service all year round, not just at holiday times.

> **(a)** Explain how delayed payments from business clients could affect Marcus's cash flow. **(2 marks)**

....

....

> **(b)** Explain how relying on family travel alone could affect his cash flow. **(2 marks)**

....

....

Guided

3 Marcus has been told that completing a cash flow forecast will help his business to be successful.

> Discuss the risks for Marcus of not doing this. **(8 marks)**

If Marcus doesn't do this some business customers may owe him money but he may not know.

....

....

....

....

....

....

> Think about the different risks and what their wider effect on the business might be.

....

....

....

Completing and analysing cash flow forecasts

1   Why is the closing balance figure so important in a cash flow forecast?
    Put a cross in the box next to the correct answer.   **(1 mark)**

A ☐ It shows how much money will have been earned from sales

B ☐ It shows whether customers are paying on time

C ☐ It shows how much money the business will have

D ☐ It shows how much money will have been spent on overheads

Guided

2   Ben has a small bakery. He is producing his cash flow forecast for three months.

Complete the cash flow statement by completing the blank cells.   **(4 marks)**

	January (£)	February (£)	March (£)
Total receipts	16,250	10,600	12,550
Total payments	12,100	12,400	10,800
Net inflow/outflow	4,150		
Opening balance	18,150		20,500
Closing balance			

Remember that the closing balance for one month is the opening balance for the next.

Complete cash flow forecasts carefully. One calculation error can impact on other entries, so check everything you do.

3   Abigail has an online retail business. She produces her cash flow forecast for three months.

	November (£)	December (£)	January (£)
Total receipts	18,000	25,000	25,000
Total payments	30,000	20,000	10,000
Net inflow/outflow	(12,000)	5,000	15,000
Opening balance	5,000	(7,000)	(2,000)
Closing balance	(7,000)	(2,000)	13,000

(a) Look at the cash flow forecast. Identify **one** major problem for Abigail's business and recommend **one** action she could take to improve the way she runs her finances.   **(2 marks)**

....

....

(b) Identify the best month for Abigail to replace her computer system.   **(1 mark)**

....

....

....

Look carefully at her closing balances before you answer this question and think about when she will have the money available!

Cost of sales

1   Which of these statements best describes cost of sales?   **(1 mark)**

   A ☐   The money spent on advertising a product

   B ☐   The budget for the sales and marketing department

   C ☐   The price paid for items used to make a product

   D ☐   The cost of moving the goods from producer to retailer

Guided   **2**   Stephanie makes cakes for special occasions, such as birthdays and weddings.

   Which **two** of the following items would be her cost of sales items?
   Circle the correct images.   **(2 marks)**

Flour

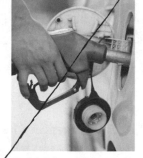

Petrol for her delivery van

> This option is not correct. Cost of sales refers to the cost of making an item, not selling it.

Icing sugar

Advertising leaflets

3   The total value of the components that go into making a bicycle is £20.

   If a cycle manufacturer makes 1,000 bikes, what is his total cost of sales?
   Put a cross in the box next to the correct answer.   **(1 mark)**

   A ☐   £200

   B ☐   £2,000

> Don't guess this because it looks easy. Check with a calculator!

   C ☐   £20,000

   D ☐   £200,000

Gross profit

> **Guided**

1 Tom wants to calculate his gross profit for the first time.

> **(a)** Write a brief definition of gross profit to help him. **(1 mark)**

Gross profit is the money made from .... a product after the

.... of producing it has been ....

> **(b)** Show him how to calculate gross profit by putting the items in the box into the formula in the correct order. **(1 mark)**

| Cost of sales | Revenue |

Gross profit = ... – ....

2 Tom sells burgers from his mobile van. He lists the cost of his materials per burger.

> Burgers = bun + burger + onions = 25p per burger

Last weekend he sold 1,200 burgers at £1 each.

> Using these figures, complete the table below. **(3 marks)**

Total sales revenue	
Total cost of sales	
Gross profit	

....

....

....

3 Tom is now thinking about buying better quality meat and selling organic burgers. He would then have to increase his selling price and thinks this could affect sales. He draws a table showing two options.

	Option A	Option B
Cost of sales per organic burger	50p	50p
Selling price	£1.50	£2
Predicted number of sales	1000	800

> Use this information to calculate his potential gross profit for both options. **(2 marks)**

Option A ....

....

....

Option B ....

....

....

The impact of positive and negative gross profit

1 | Complete the two sentences below by choosing the correct words from the box.   **(2 marks)**

revenue	expenditure	variable costs
outflows	cost of sales	inflows

You should be looking for the same two words for both sentences!

- There is a positive gross profit figure when .... is greater than the ....

- The gross profit figure is negative when the .... is greater than ....

2 Jake sells bedding plants from his garden centre.
He buys each plant for 75p and sells them for £2.00.

You can show a negative gross profit by writing it in brackets.

Guided

(a) Calculate his gross profit if he sells 500 plants a week.   **(1 mark)**

Revenue = £2 × 500 = ...

Cost of sales = £........................ × ....

Gross profit = £........................ − .... = ...

In late July, Jake sells off some surplus plants for £750. His cost of sales for these is £1,200.

(b) Calculate his gross profit figure for these plants.   **(1 mark)**

....

(c) Identify **two** benefits for Jake if he makes a positive gross profit over the summer.
    (2 marks)

1 ....

2 ....

3 Daisy runs a small café selling freshly made sandwiches, cakes and pies.

If her gross profit figure is negative, suggest **two** types of action she could take to improve her business finances.   **(2 marks)**

1 ....

2 ....

Net profit

Guided 1 Select the correct words to complete the formula for net profit. **(1 mark)**

| Revenue | Inflows | Gross profit | Cost of sales | Total costs | Expenditure |

Net profit = ... — *Expenditure*

2 Jan makes cupcakes. She has made a note of the following information.

October: Income from sales: £900

Gross profit: £700

Cost of ingredients: £200

Expenses: £250

> If you know the formula, you should know which data you need and which you don't.

Use this information to calculate her net profit. **(1 mark)**

....

3 A business owner summarises a month's trading as follows:

| Revenue £6,000   Cost of sales £2,000   Other expenses £3,000 |

Calculate the business' gross and net profit figures. **(2 marks)**

Gross profit: ....

Net profit: ....

4 Simon's accountant tells him that the gross profit for his business last year was £18,000. He tells you he intends to buy a new car with this money.

As his friend, explain **two** reasons regarding whether this is a good decision. **(4 marks)**

> Provide a linked answer when you are asked to 'explain' something.

....
....
....
....
....
....
....

The impact of positive and negative net profit

1   Sam has run his business for two years. These are his figures:

	Year 1	Year 2
Gross profit	£50,000	£50,000
Expenditure	£45,000	£56,000
Net profit	£5,000	(£6,000)

(a) Identify Sam's best year. Give a reason for your choice.   **(1 mark)**

....

(b) What is his financial situation at the moment?   **(1 mark)**

....

(c) Suggest **one** action Sam can take to improve future performance.   **(1 mark)**

....

> Guided

(d) Describe **one** likely impact on Sam's business if he fails to improve his finances.   **(2 marks)**

Sam will run out of .... and not have enough to pay his staff .... or his

.... Eventually he will have to ....

2   Mandy has made a positive net profit.

Which **one** of these statements about her business is **not** true?
Put a cross next to the answer that is not true.   **(1 mark)**

A ☐ The business made a positive gross profit

B ☐ Expenditure is less than gross profit

C ☐ Net profit is less than gross profit

D ☐ Total costs are higher than sales revenue

> Write out the formulae for gross and net profit to help work this out.

3   Identify **two** benefits for a business owner who makes a positive net profit.   **(2 marks)**

1   ....

2   ....

Financial statements

1 Mark is preparing a document that will show his assets and liabilities.

> **(a)** What is the name of this document? Put a cross in the box next to the correct answer.
> **(1 mark)**

A ☐ Income statement

B ☐ Breakeven analysis

C ☐ Cash flow forecast

D ☐ Statement of financial position

Mark is confused about the difference between assets and liabilities.

> **(b)** Define the terms 'assets' and 'liabilities'. **(2 marks)**

Assets: ....

Liabilities: ....

2 Various people may be interested in seeing the financial statements of a business.

> Draw lines to match each type of person with the reason for their interest. **(4 marks)**

Suppliers		To check their money is safely invested
Customers		To check the business can pay its debts
Shareholders		To check the business can repay a loan
Bank manager		To check it is safe to buy from them

> Start with the easiest one and leave the one you find hardest until last.

Guided 3

> Give **three** reasons why a business may prepare an income statement. **(3 marks)**

1 To check its financial activities

2 ....

3 ....

Income statement (profit and loss account)

1   State the main purpose of an income statement (profit and loss account).   **(1 mark)**

....

2   Here is an income statement for a business.

	£	£
Income from sales		50,000
Cost of sales	15,000	
Gross profit		
Expenses		
Wages and salaries	20,000	
Utilities	3,000	
Net profit		

(a) Identify the lines that make up the trading account.   **(1 mark)**

....

....

Remember this shows one type of profit only.

Guided

(b) Calculate the gross and net profit and enter these figures on the table.   **(2 marks)**

Gross profit: £50,000 − ....=...................................

Net profit: ....

Remember to show your working out.

3   Using the template below, prepare an income statement (profit and loss account) for a business using the following information.   **(6 marks)**

Income from sales £20,000   Cost of sales £5,000

Wages and salaries £8,000   Utilities £2,000

	£	£
Gross profit		
Expenses		
Net profit		

Assets, liabilities and working capital

1 Marcel runs an online delivery firm. He is trying to identify his fixed assets.

> Which **two** items are his fixed assets? Circle the correct images. **(2 marks)**

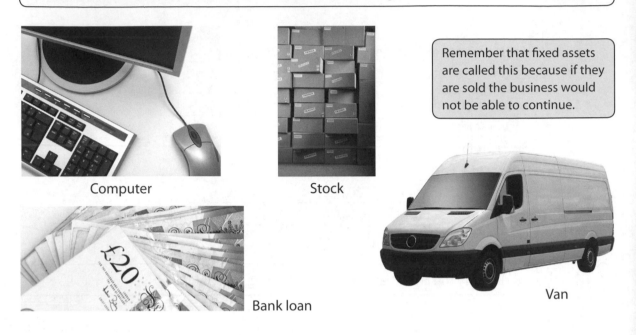

Computer

Stock

> Remember that fixed assets are called this because if they are sold the business would not be able to continue.

Van

Bank loan

Guided **2**

> State why an overdraft amount is entered under current liabilities. **(1 mark)**

An overdraft is a current liability because ....

....

> Think about why it is a liability, then think about why it is a current liability.

3 Working capital is also called net current assets. It is the current assets the business would have after paying all its current debts.

Maria has £4,000 in her business bank account. Her customers owe her £2,000.
She owes her suppliers £2,000.

> **(a)** Complete the following table to calculate her working capital. **(2 marks)**

	£
Current assets	
Current liabilities	
Working capital	

> **(b)** Explain why working capital is so important. **(2 marks)**

....

....

The statement of financial position (balance sheet)

1 Which **two** of these statements best describe a statement of financial position? **(2 marks)**

A ☐ A statement of the profit and loss made by a business

B ☐ A snapshot of a business' finances at a particular point in time

C ☐ An account of cash flow over a 12-month period

D ☐ A summary of the money invested in a business and what it has been spent on

E ☐ A summary of the liabilities of a business

2 Duncan runs a printing business and this is his statement of financial position. Use it to answer the questions below.

ASSETS	£	£
Fixed assets		
Printing equipment		10,000
Current assets		
Stock	5,000	
Trade receivables	2,000	
Cash in bank	1,000	8,000
Total assets		18,000
LIABILITIES		
Current liabilities		
Trade payables	700	
Overdraft	300	1,000
Working capital (Net current assets)		7,000
Total assets less current liabilities		17,000
Shareholders' funds		
Share capital	10,000	
Retained profit	7,000	
	17,000	

(a) State why stock, trade receivables and cash in bank are 'current assets'. **(1 mark)**

....

Duncan's accountant says that he should reduce his trade receivables figures.

> **Guided**

(b) Explain **one** way he can do this. **(2 marks)**

Make sure you understand the term 'trade receivables'.

Duncan needs to .... so that ....

(c) How much money has been invested in the business? **(2 marks)**

....

(d) Refer to the figures for working capital and explain whether the business is financially sound. **(2 marks)**

....

Completing a statement of financial position (balance sheet)

1 │ Define the term 'trade payables' and say whether these are an asset or a liability.   **(2 marks)**

....

....

> **Guided**

2 Iftekar repairs car bodywork. Enter the following items into his statement of financial position.

| Equipment/machines £12,000 | Trade receivables £2,100 | Stock £2,500 |
| Trade payables £1,600 | Cash in bank £3,000 | Overdraft £1,000 |

Complete his statement of financial position and calculate his total assets and working capital.   **(7 marks)**

ASSETS	£	£
Fixed assets		
Equipment/machines		12,000
Current assets		
Total assets		
LIABILITIES		
Current liabilities		
Overdraft	1,000	
Working capital (Net current assets)		

3 Iftekar has bought a van for £1,500 which he has paid for with money from his bank account. He has also paid a supplier £500.

Using this information, revise his statement of financial position and calculate his new working capital.   **(6 marks)**

ASSETS	£	£
Fixed assets		
Current assets		
Total assets		
LIABILITIES		
Current liabilities		
Working capital (Net current assets)		

Increasing profits and analysing an income statement (profit and loss account)

1 Last year, Duncan, a printer, successfully increased his gross profit.

> Which **two** of these actions would have had this effect? **(2 marks)**

> Think about the formula for gross profit before you answer this.

A ☐ Changing electricity supplier

B ☐ Negotiating cheaper rates for buying paper

C ☐ Moving to cheaper premises

D ☐ Increasing his prices

E ☐ Reducing his number of staff

2 Kelly has a catering business. This is her income statement.

Sales revenue	£175,000
Cost of sales	£67,000
Staff wages	£52,000
Rent and rates	£15,000
Advertising	£10,000
Gas and electric	£5,000
Telecommunications/internet	£1,000

Guided

> **(a)** Calculate her gross profit for the year. **(1 mark)**

Gross profit = £ .... − £67,000 = £ ....

> **(b)** Calculate her net profit for the year. **(1 mark)**

....

> **(c)** Explain **two** improvements she could make that would increase her net profit. **(4 marks)**

1 ....

....

2 ....

....

3 Kelly is wondering whether she should increase her prices.

> Outline **one** advantage and **one** disadvantage of this method of increasing profit. **(2 marks)**

....

....

Analysing a statement of financial position (balance sheet) for a small business

 1 Rob has been running his model shop for one year. This is his statement of financial position.

> Study it carefully and discuss what action Rob should take to improve his working capital.
>
> **(8 marks)**

ASSETS	£	£
Fixed assets		
Equipment		10,000
Motor vehicles		8,000
Current assets		
Stock	5,000	
Trade receivables	2,000	
Cash in bank	400	7,400
Total assets		25,400
LIABILITIES		
Current liabilities		
Trade payables	6,000	
Overdraft	3,000	9,000
Working capital (Net current assets)		(1,600)

Rob's working capital is negative. It means that he has not got enough money to operate the business and cannot meet his debts. Rob only has £400 cash in bank, which is not enough to pay for his day-to-day expenses.
He should ....
....
....
....
....
....
....
....

> Look at each line of the statement while answering. Think about Rob's trade payables, overdraft and working capital.

2 Twelve months later Rob's trade receivables are £5,000. Outline the danger to a small business if this figure is too high.   **(2 marks)**

....
....

Exam skills 1

For each multiple choice question, choose the correct answer(s) and put a cross in the box ☒.

On this page you can practise answering some multiple choice questions.

1   Which **one** of these is a fixed cost for a sandwich business that delivers orders to local businesses? **(1 mark)**

A ☐ Sandwich ingredients

B ☐ Road tax for van

C ☐ Petrol for van

D ☐ Wages for an assistant employed only during busy periods

〉**Guided**〉 **2**   A toy manufacturer is preparing his statement of financial position. He needs to identify his fixed and current assets.

Identify which of the **two** of the following are fixed assets. **(2 marks)**

A ☐ Computer equipment   **B** ☒ Stock of toys

C ☐ Production machinery   Stock can't be a fixed asset because it is always changing.

D ☐ Cash in the bank   **E** ☐ Staff uniforms

3   A businessman is preparing a cash flow forecast.

Which **two** of these are cash outflows? **(2 marks)**

A ☐ Sales revenue   **B** ☐ Staff wages

C ☐ Interest on a savings account   **D** ☐ Purchase of raw materials

E ☐ Share capital invested by the owner

4   Which **two** of the terms below are needed to complete the formula for gross profit? **(1 mark)**

Gross profit = ... − ....

A ☐ Sales revenue   **B** ☐ Fixed costs

C ☐ Cost of sales   **D** ☐ Expenditure

E ☐ Net profit

You need to know the formulae for both gross profit and net profit.

Exam skills 2

1   Zoe is planning to make book bags for young school children. She decides to work out how many she must sell each month to make a profit.

She writes these notes.

Fixed costs	£3,000
Variable cost per book bag	£3
Selling price per book bag	£5

(a) Calculate the break-even point using the following formula.   **(1 mark)**

$$\text{Break-even point} = \frac{\text{Fixed costs}}{\text{Selling price} - \text{Variable cost}}$$

....

Zoe's landlord informs her that he is putting up the rent on her workshop.

(b) Her fixed costs will now be £4,000. Calculate her new break-even point.   **(1 mark)**

....

Guided ▷   2   A business produces bird tables.

Calculate the total revenue in a month if it sells 200 tables at a selling price of £11 each.

    (1 mark)

Total revenue = 200 × ....

3

Complete this income statement by calculating the gross and net profit.   **(1 mark)**

	£
Sales revenue	10,000
Cost of sales	2,000
Gross profit	
Expenses	5,000
Net profit	

....

....

....

....

....

Exam skills 3

1 This is the cash flow forecast for Juan's coffee shop for June.

	£	£
Total receipts	5,000	
Total payments	1,500	
Net inflow/outflow	3,500	
Opening balance	16,000	
Closing balance	19,500	

Juan has bought some new equipment for his coffee shop. He has spent £2,000.

> **(a)** Update the forecast in the table above.   **(1 mark)**

Juan is considering building an extension before next year. This will cost £10,000.

> **(b)** Based on his financial situation, explain **one** reason why this would improve his business.   **(2 marks)**

....

....

....

> Consider the type of business, his finances, how much he would spend and the potential benefits.

2 Liam makes and sells leather bags. Although his sales are high, he has made a loss. He is puzzled. He shows you his income statement.

	£
Sales revenue	80,500
Cost of sales	60,000
Gross profit	20,500
Expenditure	30,500
Net profit	(10,000)

> **(a)** Using his income statement, explain **one** reason why this has happened.   **(2 marks)**

....

....

Guided

> **(b)** Recommend **three** actions he should take to improve his business.   **(3 marks)**

1   Increase his gross profit by buying cheaper materials so that his cost of sales is lower.

2   ....

3   ....

Defining marketing and its importance to business

Matt and Kelly have bought a small village tea room near a children's playground. There are two other cafés nearby. They plan to sell ice cream and light lunches. They have read that marketing is vital to the success of their business.

> Throughout the workbook, read each scenario carefully. Some of the questions in the assessment test are based on scenarios so this will give you good practice.

1   What is meant by the term 'marketing'?   **(1 mark)**

> If you are asked to define a marketing term, simply state what it means.

....

....

2   Matt says that gaining market share will be important.

What is the meaning of the term 'market share'?   **(1 mark)**

....

....

Guided   3   Describe **two** ways in which effective marketing can help Matt and Kelly to run their business profitably.   **(4 marks)**

> 'Describe' means give more information about the main points. In this question, think about the benefits gained by identifying and meeting customer needs. Then consider how marketing can help to encourage repeat business.

1   Through effective marketing they will identify the best products that their ....

....

....

2   ....

....

....

How businesses use marketing

Chillax is a brand of leisurewear. Sales started falling last year so the business carried out an investigation into the design and appearance that its customers wanted and why they were now buying from competitors. They then designed a new high-end range to sell in shops and stores.

1   Chillax wants to launch its new range through marketing. Identify **two** reasons why a business may use marketing.

(2 marks)

> Remember that to get both marks, you need to give **two** answers.

1   ....

....

2   ....

....

> **Guided**

2   Chillax wants to gain competitive advantage with its new range. What is the meaning of competitive advantage?

(1 mark)

Competitive advantage is the .... gained over ....

from offering .... or more attractive .... or services.

3   **(a)** For marketing purposes, identify **one** benefit to Chillax of finding out customer needs.

(1 mark)

....

....

(b) For marketing purposes, identify **one** benefit to Chillax of finding out about competitor products.

(1 mark)

....

....

(c) Explain **one** reason why Chillax has decided to offer a better quality range at the same price, to tempt customers to buy, rather than just reducing its prices.   **(2 marks)**

> Aim to write **two** linked sentences for an 'explain' question.

....

....

....

....

Marketing, corporate objectives and SMART objectives

The Chocolate Experience is a successful enterprise. It operates at two tourist resorts, offering visitors the chance to make their own chocolate and buy gift boxes. Max, its owner, aims to expand and operate in more tourist resorts. He has written a marketing plan which focuses on growing the business.

1   State **one** way Max's marketing plan should link to his corporate objective to expand the business. **(1 mark)**

> Remember that the marketing plan focuses on activities to be undertaken.

....

....

Guided   2   Complete the following table relating to SMART objectives. **(4 marks)**

	Meaning of letter	Definition
S =	Specific	
M =		Objectives are easily measured
A =		
R =		
T =		

3   Max has written the following corporate objective: to expand the business.

(a) What is the meaning of the term 'corporate objective'? **(1 mark)**

....

....

(b) Suggest **one** other corporate objective Max might have. **(1 mark)**

> There are several correct answers to this question. What would you aim to do if you were Max?

....

....

(c) Rewrite his objective so that it is SMART. **(1 mark)**

> Identify a reasonable number of new outlets he could open as well as a timescale.

....

....

B2B and B2C markets

Shazia is an interior designer. Her high street shop is stocked with attractive fabrics, small items of furniture, pictures and other decorative household items. She also orders wallpaper and makes soft furnishings, such as cushions and curtains, for her customers.

1 Shazia operates in the B2C market. What is the B2C market? **(1 mark)**

....

....

> **Guided**

2 Give **two** ways in which Shazia will market her goods and services to the B2C market. **(2 marks)**

> You buy in the B2C market so think about what tempts you to buy certain items.

1 She will carry out market research to ....

....

2 ....

....

3 Shazia's friend is an architect. He is planning a new extension for a large hotel. He asks if she would be interested in designing the bedrooms and providing the furnishings.

(a) The architect works in the B2B market. What is the B2B market? **(1 mark)**

....

....

(b) Shazia is asked to meet with the hotel owner and manager to discuss her ideas. Identify **two** factors that will be important to these business buyers. **(2 marks)**

> Remember – business buyers usually place large orders so take this into account.

1 ....

....

2 ....

....

Other types of markets

Twinkle Toes is a new brand of trainers for children. Special equipment is used to insert coloured lights in the toes and heels. These flash when the child walks. The shoes are stocked by Little Feet, a specialist shoe shop, which employs trained shoe fitters to ensure that all of the shoes that are sold fit correctly.

1 (a) Twinkle Toes are made by Bartletts, a shoe manufacturer. Identify whether Bartletts operates in the goods market, the services market or both. **(1 mark)**

> If you are asked to 'identify' then you don't have to give an explanation.

....

....

(b) Little Feet sells the shoes. Explain whether this business operates in the goods market, the services market or both. **(2 marks)**

> If you are asked to 'explain' then you need to give a reason for your choice. This will gain you an extra mark.

....

....

....

2 Bartletts uses special equipment in the factory to make the trainers. State whether this equipment is a capital good or a consumer good. Then state whether the trainers they make are a capital good or a consumer good. **(2 marks)**

> If you are asked to 'state' something then you don't have to give an explanation.

....

....

....

Guided 3 (a) Bartletts has prepared a poster for shops, such as Little Feet, explaining the benefits of the Twinkle Toes trainers to parents. Explain why this poster is not targeted at the children who will wear the shoes. **(2 marks)**

> Before you answer, think about the difference between consumers and customers.

The .... are the customers and they will make the decision

on whether or not to purchase the trainers. The decision will depend upon factors such

as .... and .... rather than

.... or flashing lights.

(b) Explain whether Little Feet operates in the mass market or a niche market. **(2 marks)**

....

....

....

Business models

Jack Flash Motors is on a main road outside a busy town. It sells second-hand cars. Most of them are over three years old. The cars are parked in rows in an open space with a small office behind. Brightly-coloured flags, bunting and slogans about cheap prices and good deals attract potential customers.

1 What is the meaning of the term 'business model'? **(1 mark)**

....

....

Guided **2** Describe Jack Flash Motors' business model.

(2 marks)

> There are three business models to choose from: sales, advertising and marketing.

Jack Flash Motors operates a sales model because ....

....

....

....

....

Jack's son, Ryan, is a website developer. He is trying to persuade his father that having a website would be good for business. He has a portfolio of all the websites he has created and details of how he has customised them for individual clients. He also regularly updates his clients' websites so that the content is fresh and appealing.

3 **(a)** Identify Ryan's business model. **(1 mark)**

....

....

(b) Explain **one** way this type of business model should enable Ryan to do well in his business. **(2 marks)**

....

....

....

....

Business orientation and choice of business model

Brian loves growing exotic plants. He started his own garden centre to sell these but only had a few local visitors. He then started a website to offer these rare plants to a wider market and has become quite an expert on rare botany. Last week he was featured on TV, which resulted in an increase in orders.

Sue is also a keen gardener but was frustrated when she couldn't buy many items she wanted locally – especially in small quantities. She set up her garden centre to provide items in small quantities. In addition, she provides plants that grow easily in the unpredictable British climate. She often gives advice to local gardeners and last year, in response to several requests, she opened a Christmas grotto for the children.

> This is a longer scenario to give you practice at reading more information. Read this at least **twice** before you start to answer any questions. Highlight any important facts. For example, the fact that Brian is an exotic plant grower and an expert on rare botany.

1 **(a)** Identify the orientation of Brian's business.

(1 mark)

> A business can be product orientated or market orientated. What is Brian's focus – his product or his customers? What is Sue's focus?

....

....

(b) Identify the orientation of Sue's business.   **(1 mark)**

....

2 **(a)** Identify Brian's business model.   **(1 mark)**

....

(b) Explain **one** reason why Brian's business will benefit from his role as an expert and the fact he sells rare plants online.   **(2 marks)**

....

....

....

3 **(a)** Identify Sue's business model.   **(1 mark)**

....

(b) Explain **one** reason why Sue's business could do well in the local environment.   **(2 marks)**

....

....

....

Branding – its importance and dimensions

Whippersnappers is a new soft play area for children with safe, modern equipment. There is an adventure area for older children and a separate area for toddlers. There is plenty of seating for parents and an eating area – all within view of the equipment. Whippersnappers also hosts children's birthday parties with the focus on the children having fun. The owners of Whippersnappers want to develop a distinctive brand to differentiate their play area from others in the area.

1   What is the meaning of the term 'brand dimensions'?   **(1 mark)**

....

....

Guided   2   Outline **three** ways in which Whippersnappers can create a distinctive brand.   **(3 marks)**

1   Whippersnappers can create a distinctive logo that people will associate with their business.

2   ....

....

....

3   ....

....

....

3   Explain why the following aspects will be important to their branding: **(4 marks)**

> Values are the good qualities of a business that the business wants to communicate to its customers.

1   Brand consistency ....

....

....

....

2   Brand values ....

....

....

....

The benefits of building brands

Marian's grandmother made wonderful chutneys and jellies from the fruit in her garden. She passed her recipes down through the family. Marian started making these a year ago. She called them Granny's Garden Produce. Sales have grown steadily and Marian has now been invited to pitch to a major supermarket chain. She now thinks it is time to focus on developing her brand properly.

Guided

1   Explain **three** benefits to Marian of having a distinctive brand for her chutneys and jellies. **(6 marks)**

> Give a reason or outcome for each benefit to get full marks.

   1   She is more likely to get repeat purchases because ....

....

....

   2   ....

....

....

   3   ....

....

....

2   Marian wants her brand to have a unique personality.

   (a) Explain **one** reason why that is important. **(2 marks)**

....

....

   (b) Outline an appropriate brand personality that Marian could adopt for her foods. **(1 mark)**

> There is no single right answer here. Suggest a personality that would appeal to buyers of her product and that is related to the name of the brand.

....

....

3   Marian sees the business expanding over the next few years. Explain **one** method she could use to grow her brand. **(2 marks)**

....

....

....

....

Market research – types and sources of data

> This case study continues throughout this learning aim to give you the opportunity to practise reading and analysing a longer scenario. This will give you practice for the case study in Section B of the assessment test.

Jacqui Evans lives on a farm in the Lake District with her brother Ivan and her parents. She is looking for ideas to start a business based on her experience with animals on the farm. She has read about the first pet café in the UK which has opened in West Yorkshire. This enables dogs and their owners to enjoy refreshments together after a walk on the fells. It serves cakes for pets that are sugar- and salt-free which are served on special plates. Jacqui now wants to find out if a pet café would be feasible where she lives.

1   Jacqui decides to carry out market research. What is meant by the term 'market research'?   **(1 mark)**

....

2   Jacqui decides to visit the tourist information office to find out how many places welcome visitors with pets in the area.

> Aim to use the word 'because' in your answers.

> **Guided**

    (a) Explain whether this data is qualitative or quantitative.   **(2 marks)**

    This data is quantitative data because it relates to numbers. In this example, it relates to the

....

....

    (b) Explain whether this data is primary or secondary.   **(2 marks)**

....

....

3   Jacqui wants to find out what visitors to the area think of her idea.

    (a) Explain whether this data is qualitative or quantitative.   **(2 marks)**

....

....

    (b) Explain whether this data is primary or secondary.   **(2 marks)**

....

....

    (c) Give **one** way she could collect this data.   **(1 mark)**

....

The uses of data to support marketing activity

This case study is a continuation of the case study on page 45.

Jacqui has completed her research. She has found that most people with dogs live locally or they are day visitors with little interest in a pet café. They told her that many cafés now have outside eating areas where dogs are welcome. Holidaymakers said they left their pets at home because very few hotels, guest houses or apartments allow dogs. The tourist information office confirmed this. They also told her that visitor numbers to the area are rising because more people are holidaying in the UK. The number of people coming on day trips is also increasing.

1 Explain whether or not the data Jacqui obtained shows a demand for a pet café locally. **(2 marks)**

> Consider what has been found before coming to a conclusion and give a reason for your decision.

....

....

....

....

Guided ▷ **2** Identify **three** market trends in Jacqui's area. **(2 marks)**

> To identify a trend, look for something that is changing in some way.

1   More and more cafés have outdoor eating areas

2   ....

....

3   ....

....

3 Jacqui thinks she has found a gap in the market as very little holiday accommodation allows pets.

(a) What is meant by the term 'gap in the market'? **(1 mark)**

....

....

(b) Explain **one** way Jacqui can benefit from finding this gap. **(2 marks)**

....

....

....

....

The uses of internal and external data and situational analysis

> This case study is a continuation of the case study on pages 45–46.

Jacqui and her family decide the farm needs to increase its income. Her brother, Ivan, thinks that the work involved in opening pet-friendly holiday accommodation would take time away from the farm itself. One alternative idea is to turn the farm itself into a visitor attraction. Jacqui would like an area where visitors can handle and pet the chicks and baby lambs, a hay barn for children to play, a tea room and outside play area, and a path for walking past the donkeys, sheep, goats and hens. Ivan can offer horse riding, and barrel rides pulled by his tractor. Their parents will only provide financial backing if market research proves that the attraction could be a success.

1   Jacqui wants to benchmark her planned attraction against her competitors.

   (a) What is meant by the term 'benchmarking'?   **(1 mark)**

   ....

> Guided

   (b) Identify **two** types of information Jacqui could obtain about her competitors that will be helpful.   **(2 marks)**

   1   Information on their facilities

   2   ....

   ....

2   Jacqui decides to carry out a situational analysis.

   (a) What is meant by the term 'situational analysis'?   **(1 mark)**

   ....

   (b) Jacqui decides to produce a SWOT analysis. Complete the following table to identify what these letters represent.   **(3 marks)**

Strengths
W
O
T

   (c) Give **one** reason why carrying out a SWOT analysis will be helpful to Jacqui's business plans.   **(1 mark)**

   ....

MidKent College

The purpose of market research and analysis

> This case study is a continuation of the case study on pages 45–47.

Jacqui and Ivan are planning the visitor attraction. They will have a limited budget and have to decide which facilities and features will be the most important to their customers. Their parents have asked for further information before they agree to invest any money in the enterprise. They both realise that they must research their target market and market trends more thoroughly.

1 **(a)** What is meant by the term 'target market'? **(1 mark)**

....

....

(b) Give **two** benefits that Jacqui and Ivan will gain if they understand their target market and the behaviour of potential customers. **(2 marks)**

1 ....

2 ....

2 Give **one** reason why Jacqui and Ivan should investigate the activities of their competitors. **(1 mark)**

....

....

Guided **3** Jacqui is investigating market trends. Explain **two** reasons why she should do this. **(6 marks)**

> A plan for this answer could be:
> • Identify **two** items of information she could investigate under 'market trends'.
> • For each of these, explain how it will help her to understand her business better.

....

....

....

....

....

....

....

....

Interpreting key market research findings

> This case study is a continuation of the case study on pages 45–48

Ivan has been doing some research. He has read that the UK food market is worth over £160 billion. Although supermarkets dominate the market, the number of farm shops has been increasing in the last few years. There are now several thousand. Market research shows that 50 per cent of people in the UK prefer to buy local produce because they trust the quality more than supermarket produce. This figure is increasing.

Ivan suggests that they also open a farm shop selling fresh fruit from the orchard, fresh vegetables, dairy produce, eggs, meat from their rare breed of pigs, and homemade cakes and pies. They could also make up vegetables boxes for local people.

1   What is meant by the term 'market growth'?   **(1 mark)**

....

....

Guided   2   **(a)** A farm shop supplies a 'niche market'. What is meant by the term 'niche market'?   **(1 mark)**

A niche market is a ...., ... market (or group of

customers) that concentrates on a .... product.

(b) Identify **two** examples from Ivan's research that support his idea to open a farm shop.   **(2 marks)**

> Look for **two** examples that focus on farm shops. The total value of the UK food market is not relevant because this refers to the mass market for food.

....

....

....

....

3   As the farm shop is a niche market it will only have a small market share, but this is often better for small businesses. Give **two** benefits of supplying a niche market.   **(2 marks)**

1   ....

....

2   ....

....

PESTLE analysis

> This case study is a continuation of the case study on pages 45–49.

Jacqui and Ivan decide to carry out a PESTLE analysis on their farm shop idea. The results show that they may need planning permission to convert their barn and that, to be successful in the area, they must sell local produce. Lots of advice is available on government websites. The government wants more farm shops as this provides more income for farmers and increases the amount of food produced in the UK. Farm shops also reduce food miles and use less packaging than supermarkets.

The economy is doing better and at present people have more money to spend. They are spending more in farm shops but are also increasingly shopping for food online. The current trend for many people to take holidays in the UK should help visitor numbers, although high fuel prices sometimes deter people from driving very far. Ivan says they could counteract this by having a website and selling online, as well as having a physical shop.

1   Complete the table below to show what the letters in PESTLE represent.   **(3 marks)**

| **P**olitical |
| **E** |
| **S** |
| **T**echnological |
| **L** |
| **E**nvironmental |

2   Carry out a PESTLE analysis for Jacqui and Ivan and identify **one** relevant factor for each heading.   **(6 marks)**

....

....

....

....

 3   Use your analysis to evaluate their idea to run a farm shop.   **(8 marks)**

> A plan for your answer could be:
> • Identify **two** positive aspects of their idea.
> • Identify **two** negative aspects of their idea.
> • Think about whether or not these mean that their enterprise is likely to be successful.

....

....

....

....

....

....

....

....

The marketing mix – an overview

This case study continues throughout this learning aim to give you the opportunity to apply your knowledge to a new and developing business. This will give you further practice for case studies in the assessment test.

Choca2 is a new type of chocolate biscuit developed by two friends, Asiya and Bethany. The biscuits are flavoured with cardamom – an oriental spice. The biscuits were so popular with friends and family that the girls have decided to start their own business with the brand name Choca2. They trial their biscuits at a local summer fête but are disappointed when sales are low. Imran, Asiya's cousin, works in marketing. He tells them that they need to identify the right marketing mix for their product.

1   What is the meaning of the term 'marketing mix'?   **(1 mark)**

....

....

2   Complete the 4 Ps that make up the marketing mix.   **(2 marks)**

| **P**roduct |
| **P** |
| **P**lace |
| **P** |

⟩ **Guided** ⟩   **3**   Explain how focusing on **two** elements of the marketing mix will help Asiya and Bethany to launch a successful business.   **(4 marks)**

> Your answer should give an example of how each element of the marketing mix can help them make the best decision.

Asiya and Bethany must consider all aspects of the marketing mix. This will help them

focus on the needs of their target customers. Under 'product' they must assess the look

of the product, the taste, the packaging and the brand name to see if these will appeal to

their target customers.

....

....

....

....

....

....

....

....

Product differentiation

> This case study is a continuation of the case study on page 51.

Imran says that they have several tasks to carry out before they launch their biscuits. Firstly, they need to decide how to differentiate their biscuits to make them different and appealing to customers.

1 (a) Define the term 'USP'. **(1 mark)**

....

....

(b) Identify the main USP of the Choca2 biscuits. **(1 mark)**

> Look back at the case study on the previous page and reread that information before you answer this question.

....

....

2 Describe **two** ways in which Asiya and Bethany can augment the basic product so that it is even more appealing. **(4 marks)**

1 ....

....

....

....

2 ....

....

....

....

Guided **3** Explain why it is important to differentiate the biscuits in some way. **(2 marks)**

There are many types of biscuits on the market. As these are special spiced biscuits it is

important to ....

....

....

....

....

Product life cycle

This case study is a continuation of the case study on pages 51–52.

Choca2 spicy biscuits, flavoured with cardamom, are about to be launched in the local market. Imran warns that the initial interest in their new product will not last very long. He advises Asiya and Bethany to think about what they should do if sales of these biscuits fall in the future.

Guided

1 Complete the missing stages of the product life cycle.   **(2 marks)**

Development/Introduction

....

Maturity

....

2 **(a)** In which stage of the life cycle are Choca2 biscuits when they are launched?   **(1 mark)**

....

(b) Identify **two** key characteristics of this stage.   **(2 marks)**

> Think about the levels of sales and profits before you answer this question. These vary at all stages of the product life cycle.

1 ....

....

2 ....

....

3 **(a)** What is meant by the term 'extension strategy'?   **(1 mark)**

....

(b) Identify **two** possible extension strategies that Choca2 could use to boost sales of their biscuits in the future.   **(2 marks)**

1 ....

....

2 ....

....

Product portfolios

> This case study is a continuation of the case study on pages 51–53.

Asiya and Bethany think it would be a good idea to extend their product range. They would then be less dependent on sales of the cardamom biscuits. Asiya wants to introduce more biscuits with different Eastern spices. Bethany wants a more varied portfolio with completely new products, such as spiced chocolate cupcakes, spiced cookies, spiced brownies and spiced ice cream.

1 What is meant by the term 'product portfolio'?   **(1 mark)**

....

2 Give **two** reasons why it is important for businesses to analyse their product portfolio
   regularly.   **(2 marks)**

1 ....

....

2 ....

....

> **Guided**

3 Asiya is in favour of keeping their product portfolio small and focused on their core product,
   while Bethany wants to broaden it by introducing a wide range of other products.
   Evaluate these options for the Choc2 business.   **(8 marks)**

> Here is a plan you could use for your answer:
> - Explain the advantages of having a small product portfolio.
> - Identify several disadvantages of a small product portfolio – these will be the advantages of a broader portfolio.

Asiya's idea has several advantages. Keeping the product portfolio small will mean that

they will spend less money on developing new products, that they will need less space for

storage of various ingredients and bakeware and that they can focus on the products they

know well and that their customers will associate with their brand. There are also several

drawbacks with keeping the portfolio very narrow. The disadvantages of a ....

....

....

....

....

....

....

....

Pricing strategies

This case study is a continuation of the case study on pages 51–54.

Choca2 owners, Asiya and Bethany, have to decide on a pricing strategy for their biscuits. They are aware that they will be operating in a competitive market – there are lots of firms making other types of biscuits. They cannot decide whether to calculate how much it costs to make the biscuits and add on a percentage markup, or whether to ask a high price because their product is different. Alternatively, they could ask a low price to gain people's interest or set a price that is the same as their competitors.

1 What is the meaning of the term 'pricing strategy'?   **(1 mark)**

....

2 Identify the **four** pricing strategies that Asiya and Bethany are considering.   **(4 marks)**

  1 ....

  2 ....

  3 ....

  4 ....

Guided

3 Select any **two** appropriate pricing strategies for the Choca2 biscuits and, for each one, explain the benefits and drawbacks.   **(6 marks)**

> Cost plus pricing is normally used by tradesmen more than by food producers; skimming is normally used by technology or drug companies who ask a high price at the launch of a revolutionary new product before competitor products are available, so don't choose either of these options.

Premium pricing would mean that they maximise their .... because prices are

.... and customers will associate their brand with .... The disadvantage

is that ....

....

....

....

....

....

....

....

....

....

....

Elasticity of demand

This case study is a continuation of the case study on pages 51–55.

Asiya and Bethany have now started selling their biscuits online, direct to customers. Demand is high and stocks are running down quickly. Asiya says this is because their price is too low. Bethany is worried that if they increase the price, demand will fall and they will do very little trade.

To test this, Imran tells them that they could change the price and then measure the change in demand. They will then find out whether or not their price should be increased.

Guided 1 What is the meaning of the term 'price elasticity of demand'? **(1 mark)**

Price elasticity of demand relates to the fact that demand for most goods usually

.... when prices .... and vice versa.

2 If demand for the biscuits is elastic, explain what will happen when the price is increased. **(2 marks)**

> Answer this precisely by saying whether demand will fall by **more** or **less** than the price increase. Just saying it will fall or rise will not gain full marks.

....

....

....

....

3 The price of the biscuits is increased by 10 per cent. Demand falls by 2 per cent.

(a) Calculate the PED of the biscuits using the following formula. **(1 mark)**

> Be careful to get your numbers the right way round!

$$PED = \frac{\% \text{ change in quantity demanded}}{\% \text{ change in price}}$$

....

(b) Explain whether this PED means the price should be lowered, stay the same or be increased even further. **(2 marks)**

> Remember – most firms want to maximise sales revenue.

....

....

....

....

Place – distribution channels

This case study is a continuation of the case study on pages 51–56

Choca2 biscuits are selling well and a large farm shop in the area has invited them to pitch to sell their biscuits through the store. If they were able to sell through the farm shop they would be able to sell in larger quantities and concentrate their own efforts on making the biscuits. Asiya thinks this is a good idea but Bethany says she would prefer that they sold to customers directly. Imran suggests that they think about the best distribution channels for their product.

1 What is the meaning of the term 'distribution channels'? **(1 mark)**

....

....

2 Identify **three** direct distribution channels that Choca2 could use to sell to customers. **(3 marks)**

> Remember that a direct channel has no intermediaries.

1 ....

2 ....

3 ....

Guided

3 Choca2 has the option of selling directly to customers or to the farm shop, which would sell their biscuits to the public. At the moment, Choca2 cannot make enough biscuits to sell through both channels. Evaluate the strengths and weaknesses of both options. **(8 marks)**

> Here is a suggested plan for your answer:
> • Think about all the benefits they would gain by selling directly to customers.
> • Think of possible problems from selling directly to customers.
> • Think of the advantages of selling to the retailer and any disadvantages.
> Two possible issues of selling to the retailer could be whether they could produce the quantities required and what would happen if sales at the farm shop were poor.

....

....

....

....

....

....

....

....

....

Place – business location

> This case study is a continuation of the case study on pages 51–57

Asiya and Bethany decide to make the biscuits for the farm shop and the product is selling well. However, they are also still keen on selling their own biscuits through other channels. Demand has increased and they think that they should find a bigger and better location for their production facility. Asiya wants to move away from selling at farmers' markets and fêtes and open a small shop in a nearby market town. She knows that they must be careful about its location because they want to promote a brand image of wholesome and high-quality biscuits. Bethany thinks that they would be better simply selling online. She thinks that if they do that their location will not matter.

> **Guided**

1 State **three** factors that will influence the location of their production facility. **(3 marks)**

> Unless they are planning a factory shop, passing trade is not important.

    1   Their production facility needs to be near to suppliers because they will need to buy ingredients

    2   ....

    3   ....

2 If they decide to open a small shop, state **two** factors that will be important when they decide on its location. **(2 marks)**

    1   ....

         ....

         ....

    2   ....

         ....

         ....

3 Identify **two** additional factors about location that will need to be taken into account if the biscuits are to be sold online. **(2 marks)**

    1   ....

         ....

         ....

    2   ....

         ....

         ....

The promotional mix, budget and channels

This case study is a continuation of the case study on pages 51–58

Choca2 is about to launch a new range of spiced biscuits that will include flavours such as cinnamon, ginger and nutmeg. Some of the biscuits will come in gift packs and will be ideal as presents. Asiya and Bethany want to promote the launch to increase sales generally and as part of their aim to develop a higher profile for their brand. They decide to focus on identifying the best promotional mix for their budget.

1 What is meant by the term 'promotional mix'?　**(1 mark)**

....

....

2 Explain **one** reason why it is important for a business to have a promotional budget.　**(2 marks)**

....

....

....

....

> **Guided**

3 Describe **three** 'below the line' promotional methods that would enable them to launch their new biscuits without spending too much money.　**(6 marks)**

> Remember that 'below the line' does not include paid-for promotions such as TV, radio and press adverts.

1　Sales promotions, such as competitions, point-of-sale materials or free gifts will ....

....

....

2　..

....

....

3　..

....

....

Viral marketing and guerilla advertising

This case study is a continuation of the case study on pages 51–59

Asiya plans to create a Facebook page for Choca2. Bethany is already a keen Twitter user. They hold a meeting to share all their ideas about using social media to promote the business. They think that they could publish recipes on Facebook and Twitter or film the biscuits being made and post this on YouTube. They could also ask a group of students at the local college to dress up and give out free samples at a local food fair to get free publicity.

1 What is meant by the term 'social media'? **(1 mark)**

....

2 Explain **two** ways in which using social media can enable Choca2 to benefit from viral marketing. **(4 marks)**

1 ....

....

2 ....

....

Guided **3** Evaluate the idea of using the guerrilla advertising tactic of a flash mob at the food fair to promote their brand. **(8 marks)**

> When you evaluate you must give a balanced argument. This means identifying the same number of relevant good points as bad points. In this question, think about the benefits of doing something different and the dangers. Then come to a conclusion and say what would be best for their business.

Guerrilla marketing using a flash mob is usually a very cheap way of getting publicity.

....

....

....

The disadvantage is that ....

....

....

Therefore, ...

....

....

Consistency and the marketing mix

This case study is a continuation of the case study on pages 51–60.

Choca2 biscuits are selling well in the small shop and online. Asiya and Bethany now want to expand and sell their biscuits over a wider area. They have decided to do this through established retailers and have the choice of pitching to several different firms, including an exclusive department store with a luxury food hall, a supermarket chain with a reputation for good-quality food and a discount chain.

1   Explain why it is important that all elements of the marketing mix are consistent.   **(2 marks)**

....

....

2   Explain how the brand image of a business can be affected by the following aspects of its marketing mix: **(4 marks)**

Product: ....

....

....

Price: ....

....

....

Guided

3   Asiya and Bethany have to choose between the three different types of retailers for selling their biscuits. Bearing in mind their brand image, evaluate each of these options.   **(8 marks)**

> To do this, think about each different 'place' and its image, the effect on the price and how the products would be promoted in each one. Ideally all these aspects should be consistent with the marketing mix and brand image of Choca2.

The exclusive department store with a luxury food hall would attract .... customers.

It would set .... prices and promote the ranges to appeal to certain customers.

The biscuits would be judged on ....

....

....

....

....

....

....

Ebusiness and ecommerce

This case study is a continuation of the case study on pages 51–61.

Selling the biscuits on a national basis has made a major difference to Choca2. They now employ more staff to deal with orders. To fulfil these orders promptly they need to check stock levels regularly. They also need to check that invoices are sent out promptly and that payments (both in and out) are monitored. They therefore decide to invest in linking all these areas by technology. This means that stock levels update automatically whenever an order is fulfilled or new batches of biscuits are ready for despatch. It also means that Asiya and Bethany can check sales, stock levels and production easily on their computers.

Guided

1 Explain the difference between ebusiness and ecommerce. **(2 marks)**

> Do this by explaining what ebusiness means and then what ecommerce means.

Ecommerce means selling or buying goods online and it may also include offering customer

service online. Ebusiness is ....

....

2 When Choca2 first started in business, they sold biscuits online.
Outline **three** benefits of having this type of business operation. **(3 marks)**

1 ....

....

2 ....

....

3 ....

....

3 Choca2 now has all its major business areas linked by technology. Outline **three** advantages of doing this. **(3 marks)**

> If you read the case study carefully you should be able to identify at least two!

1 ....

....

2 ....

....

3 ....

....

Influences on the marketing mix

This case study is a continuation of the case study on pages 51–62.

Choca2 has been in business for three years. Its products are now found in many shops and stores. However, rising inflation has meant that energy prices and wages have risen so the cost of running the business is much higher. The business may have to increase prices unless it can find a more efficient way of making the biscuits. In addition, the new focus on healthy, low-fat and low-sugar foods is affecting sales, although Asiya thinks that the older people who buy their biscuits will be less bothered about this. However, the older people who buy their biscuits will not be happy about any price increases Choca2 may need to implement. Choca2 also wants to address customer complaints about excess packaging in its gift boxes and concerns about whether this is recyclable.

Guided

1 (a) There are many factors that affect the Choca2 marketing mix.
         Give **one** factor for each of the following areas: **(3 marks)**

   • **Economic issues:** rising inflation means that cost prices are ....

   • Social issues: ....

   ....

   • Environmental issues: ....

   ....

   (b) For each factor you have given, suggest how this may affect their marketing mix.   **(3 marks)**

   1 ....

   ....

   ....

   2 ....

   ....

   ....

   3 ....

   ....

   ....

2 Explain **one** way that changes in technology could have a further influence on the marketing mix and help Asiya and Bethany.   **(2 marks)**

> Some influences can benefit businesses and help to increase profits. Think about how new technology can do this.

....

....

Evaluating the effectiveness of the marketing mix

This case study is a continuation of the case study on pages 51–63

Asiya and Bethany want to evaluate the effectiveness of their marketing mix. Last year they set a target of increasing sales by 5 per cent. When they measured the result they found that they did very well up to Christmas but then sales dipped. They have therefore missed their target and only increased sales by 3 per cent over the whole year. As they are considering buying new high technology production equipment they need to be more certain that sales will grow or this investment will be too expensive.

1   Explain **one** reason why it is important for businesses to review their marketing mix regularly.   **(2 marks)**

> Start by thinking back to all the factors that influence the marketing mix and their impact.

....

....

....

2   Explain **one** way that Asiya and Bethany can check if their sales target was 'SMART'.   **(2 marks)**

....

....

....

Guided   3   For each area of the marketing mix, suggest **one** aspect that Asiya and Bethany could consider changing to help achieve their next sales target.   **(4 marks)**

> Reread the information on page 63 on the factors that influence their marketing mix before you answer this.

Product: ....

....

Price: They could see if there is any scope for lowering the price (or not increasing it) if they buy the new equipment.

Place: ....

....

Promotion: ....

....

Exam skills 1

On this page you can practise answering questions that are not related to a case study. These focus on your knowledge of marketing and the terms used. You may find these types of question in Section A of the assessment test.

1 Give **two** reasons why marketing is important to business. **(2 marks)**

1 ....

....

2 ....

....

2 What is the meaning of the term 'product-orientated business'? **(1 mark)**

> Think about Dyson or Apple – and remember the opposite is being 'market orientated' and asking customers what they want.

....

> Guided

3 State **three** reasons why businesses use market research. **(3 marks)**

1 To identify a gap in the market

2 ....

....

3 ....

....

4 Give **one** example of 'above the line' promotion. **(1 mark)**

....

5 Identify **two** different influences on the marketing mix of a business. **(2 marks)**

1 ....

....

2 ....

....

Exam skills 2

> On this page you will practise answering questions based on a short case study. You must apply your knowledge of marketing to that particular business. You will find this type of case study in Section A.

Accent Accessories is about to launch on the high street in direct competition with established accessories stores. Its adverts claim it is special because it groups all its products into different colour ranges with accent colours – hence the name. Its target market is female, aged 13–35 years and it promises them that its prices will be unbelievably low.

1 State the USP of Accent Accessories. **(1 mark)**

....

2 Describe **two** benefits to Accent Accessories of identifying its target market. **(4 marks)**

1 ....

....

2 ....

....

3 Accent Accessories is keen to build a distinctive brand for its target market. Identify **two** dimensions of a distinctive brand. **(2 marks)**

1 ....

2 ....

Guided   **4** Explain **three** ways in which Accent Accessories can use social media to promote its stores. **(3 marks)**

> Think about information they can gain as well as provide.

1   Using social media, like Facebook and/or Twitter, will enable Accent Accessories to

     spread information about its stores quickly and cheaply to potential customers.

2 ....

....

3 ....

....

5 Research shows that the accessories market is still growing, although more slowly than in the past. State **two** ways the features of the growth stage of the product life cycle impact on businesses such as Accent Accessories. **(2 marks)**

> Reread the case study for several clues!

....

....

Exam skills 3

> This page gives you practice in considering and evaluating issues relating to Accent Accessories. This is a skill you may need for both Section A and Section B.

1 Describe how **one** economic factor may affect the marketing mix of Accent Accessories.

(2 marks)

....

....

....

....

....

> If you see the word 'economic' think money! Economic factors relate to how much money people have to spend because of falling/rising unemployment, falling/rising inflation, interest rates and taxes. Identify **one** factor and then relate it to the marketing mix.

2 Accent Accessories' products will only be available to buy in the stores and not online. The website will simply showcase the products.

(a) Give **two** factors it must bear in mind when choosing where to locate a store.   **(4 marks)**

1 ....

....

2 ....

....

> Guided

(b) Evaluate its decision not to have an ecommerce site to sell goods online.

(8 marks)

> When evaluating, identify the plus and minus points related to an issue and give a balanced view, together with a reasoned conclusion.

The benefits to Accent Accessories of having an ecommerce site are people would be able to

....

....

....

The disadvantages to Accent Accessories of having

an ecommerce site are ....

....

....

> Think about the relevance of different distribution channels to the type of business and what it sells. Also, think about the costs of ecommerce and the pricing strategy of Accent Accessories.

....

....

The conclusion is that ....

....

....

Unit 2: Practice assessment test

You have one hour to complete this assessment.
The total number of marks is 50.

1 | Which **two** of these is expenditure for a garage? Put a cross in the box next to the two correct answers. **(2 marks)** |

   A ☐ Second hand car sales

   B ☐ Revenue from servicing cars

   C ☐ Staff wages

   D ☐ MOT testing

   E ☐ Rent for the garage

2   Outdoor World is a small business selling camping equipment.

| Give **two** examples of start-up costs the business would have had. **(2 marks)** |

....

....

3 | Which **one** of these is a running cost for a newly opened flower shop? Put a cross in the box next to the correct answer. **(1 mark)** |

   A ☐ Advertising the opening of the shop

   B ☐ Obtaining a bank loan

   C ☐ Heating the shop

   D ☐ Flower sales

4   Sammy runs a pizza business and offers a home-delivery service.

| Which **two** of these are variable costs the business may have? Put a cross in the box next to the two correct items. **(2 marks)** |

   A ☐ Delivery boxes

   B ☐ Rent on property

   C ☐ Road tax on delivery van

   D ☐ MOT testing

   E ☐ Brick ovens for the pizzas

5   Jack plans to start designing and printing T-shirts. He has estimated the following monthly costs if he sells 600 items.

| A variable cost of £7 for each item he sells | Total fixed costs of £3,000 |

(a) Calculate the total variable costs of Jack's business and enter this figure on the table below.   **(1 mark)**

(b) Enter Jack's fixed costs on the table below. Then calculate his total costs.   **(1 mark)**

	600 items sold
Variable costs	£
Fixed costs	£
Total costs	£

6   Megan runs a small café and rents out the flat above. She is completing a cash flow forecast for her business and wants to identify her cash outflows.

Which **two** of these are cash outflows? Put a cross in two of the boxes.   **(2 marks)**

A ☐   Payments from customers

B ☐   Insurance

C ☐   Electricity bill

D ☐   Refund from supplier

E ☐   Rent from tenant

7   A grower sells his plants for £6 each. Last year he sold 8,000 plants.

Calculate the total revenue for the business.   **(2 marks)**

....

8   Ali runs a successful water cooler business. He employs 20 people. A new employee is puzzled when he hears the term 'budgetary control'.

Explain **one** advantage to the business of carrying out budgetary control.   **(2 marks)**

....

....

9   The owner of a party shop is analysing data about the business and plans to create a break-even chart.

Outline what is meant by the term 'breakeven'.   **(1 mark)**

....

10 Here is a break-even chart for a business.

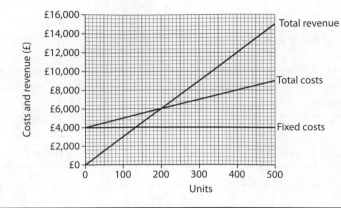

(a) Identify each of the following areas by marking them on the chart with the letter shown.

(3 marks)

| **A** The break-even point | **B** The profit area | **C** The loss area |

(b) What is the total revenue if the business sells 400 units? **(1 mark)**

....

11 A small business makes chiller cabinets. The table shows their predicted figures for the next year.

	£
Selling price per cabinet	600
Variable cost per cabinet	400
Fixed costs	50,000

The formula to calculate breakeven is:

$$\text{Break-even point} = \frac{\text{Fixed costs}}{\text{Selling price per unit} - \text{Variable cost per unit}}$$

How many chiller cabinets would the business need to sell to break even? **(1 mark)**

....

12 Lavan wants to calculate his net profit.

Which of the following figures must he subtract from his gross profit? Put a cross in the box next to the correct answer **(1 mark)**

A ☐ Expenditure

B ☐ Overheads

C ☐ Sales revenue

D ☐ Variable costs

13 John owns a printing business. He produces the following cash flow forecast for three months.

2014	July (£)	August (£)	September (£)
Total Receipts	10,000	10,000	12,000
Total Payments	8,000	10,000	10,000
Net Inflow/Outflow	2,000	0	2,000
Opening Balance	3,200	5,200	5,200
Closing Balance	5,200	5,200	7,200

(a) Describe the main purpose of a cash flow forecast. **(2 marks)**

....

....

....

John has decided to replace some old printing equipment in September. A new machine would cost him £10,000.

(b) Use the table below to calculate his new cash flow forecast. **(2 marks)**

2014	July (£)	August (£)	September (£)
Total receipts	10,000	10,000	
Total payments	8,000	10,000	
Net Inflow/Outflow	2,000	0	
Opening balance	3,200	5,200	
Closing balance	5,200	5,200	

(c) Recommend **two** actions John could take to ensure that this purchase does not have a negative effect on the business. **(2 marks)**

....

....

14

Which **one** of these is a cost of sales for Sajida, who runs a photography business? Put a cross in the box against the correct answer. **(1 mark)**

A ☐ Paying a builder to extend her studio

B ☐ Buying a car so she can visit her clients

C ☐ Buying photographic paper and photo frames

D ☐ Paying wages to her assistant

15 Paula is an interior designer and makes curtains and cushions. She is preparing her statement of financial position (balance sheet). She needs to identify which items are liabilities.

> Which **two** of these are liabilities? Put a cross in the correct boxes.   **(2 marks)**

A ☐ Money owed to suppliers

B ☐ Her sewing machines

C ☐ Bank loan

D ☐ Stock of fabrics

E ☐ Delivery van

16 Keiran runs an online retail business and employs six staff. The figures in the table are from an income statement (profit and loss account) for one year of his business.

Sales of products	£350,000
Rent	£30,000
Cost of sales	£210,000
Staff wages	£100,000
Postage and packing costs	£40,000

The net profit for his business is (£30,000) for the year.

> Describe **two** ways in which Keiran can improve his net profit for the following year.   **(4 marks)**

....

....

....

....

17 The following items are to be entered into the income statement (profit and loss account) for a pottery business.

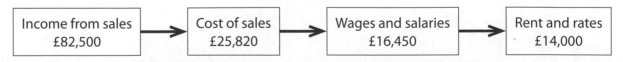

| Income from sales £82,500 | → | Cost of sales £25,820 | → | Wages and salaries £16,450 | → | Rent and rates £14,000 |

> Using this information, complete the income statement (profit and loss account).   **(3 marks)**

	£	£
Cost of sales		
Gross profit		
Expenses		
Net profit		

18 Julie started her business last year. This is an extract from her statement of financial position (balance sheet) at the end of the year.

	£	£
Fixed assets		
Equipment		3,200
Current assets		
Stock	600	
Trade receivables	3,700	
Cash in bank	400	4,700
Total assets		7,900
Current liabilities		
Trade payables	400	
Overdraft	1,100	1,500
Working capital (Net current assets)		3,200

Use this extract to describe **two** short-term actions Julie could take to improve the financial position of the business. **(4 marks)**

....
....
....
....

19 Jason and Kate want to open a doggie day care centre and combine this with pet sitting, dog walking and pet grooming. They want their business to be successful and have carefully planned their enterprise using tools including breakeven analysis, cash flow forecasting and budgeting.

Discuss how they can measure their success and identify areas for improvement.   **(8 marks)**

....
....
....
....
....
....
....
....
....
....
....
....
....
....

Unit 9: Practice assessment test

You have 1 hour 30 minutes to complete this assessment.
The total number of marks is 50.

SECTION A

1   Give a definition of marketing.   **(1 mark)**

....

....

2   Name the missing stage of a PESTLE analysis.   **(1 mark)**

    P   Political

    E   Economic

    S   Social

    T   ....

    L   Legal

    E   Environmental

3   What is the meaning of the term 'B2B market'?   **(1 mark)**

....

....

4   Describe **one** way a business may benefit from entering a slow growing market.   **(2 marks)**

....

....

....

5   Give **one** example of an indirect distribution channel.   **(1 mark)**

....

6   A small business, called You Learn Software, is a leading producer of mobile educational games aimed at children between 6 and 12 years of age. The games are free to download but these downloads contain adverts for various products, aimed at parents and children. The revenue from these adverts is used by You Learn Software to develop new products. To obtain the version with no adverts, buyers must pay £1.99.

    (a)   Identify the business model used by You Learn Software.   **(1 mark)**

....

    (b)   You Learn Software obtains quantitative data by analysing market trends and sales figures. Outline **two** ways that You Learn Software could obtain qualitative data to inform its marketing decisions.   **(2 marks)**

      1   ....

      2   ....

(c) Describe **two** benefits to You Learn Software of carrying out market research.   **(4 marks)**

1 ....

....

2 ....

....

(d) You Learn Software was founded by two software developers who have always been product orientated. As the industry is very competitive, and mobile games only have a short product life cycle, the Marketing Director is considering changing the company to a market orientation. Evaluate whether a product or a market orientation is more appropriate for You Learn Software.   **(8 marks)**

....

....

....

....

....

....

....

....

....

....

....

....

....

....

....

....

....

....

....

....

....

....

....

SECTION B

Guy's Bedrooms is a UK business that specialises in designing and installing customised fitted wardrobes and bedroom furniture. The business is owned by Emma and Steven Guy and they employ six staff. They run the business from a workshop and a design studio in a business park on the edge of town. They supply bedrooms direct to customers who visit their studio or request a design consultation in their home.

Guy's Bedrooms is advertised through its website, through small adverts in the local press and in the Yellow Pages. Emma and Steven make themselves known to potential customers on new housing estates by distributing leaflets door to door. They do this because they know that many new houses lack storage space. Making friends with several builders and decorators in the district has meant that they are often recommended to clients. Last year, the company was featured on a home makeover programme which aired on national television for several weeks. This boosted business considerably.

Customers who visit the design studio view model bedrooms and can see the range of finishes and styles available. There is a brochure that they can take home available and Emma is an expert on interior storage and colour schemes. They both visit customer's homes, by appointment, to measure a room and prepare a computerised drawing showing customers their new furniture in the room.

Emma and Steven are keen to talk to customers about their personal requirements. Because they make the furniture themselves they can cater to most requests. This is an advantage over many large national firms who only provide furniture to specific sizes. Often customers will make useful comments and suggestions that provide good ideas for future items.

Emma and Steven always aim to beat a competitor's price; they are helped by having fewer overheads than large national firms. They calculate exactly how much it costs to make each bedroom and then add on a percentage profit.

In recent years, several national competitors have increased their prices and closed many small, local showrooms. They all have sophisticated websites and glossy, professional brochures, which Guy's Bedrooms cannot afford to produce. They prefer to rely on their expertise and personal service instead.

7   Promotion is an important part of the marketing mix for Guy's Bedrooms.
    Identify **one** example of **each** of these promotions used by Guy's Bedrooms.   **(2 marks)**

Above the line: ....

Below the line: ....

8   Give **two** benefits Guy's Bedrooms gain by having a USP.   **(2 marks)**

1   ....

2   ....

9   Guy's Bedrooms knows its competitors' products and their prices. It also listens to customers and aims to meet their needs.
    State the business orientation of Guy's Bedrooms.   **(1 mark)**

....

10 Emma and Steven want Guy's Bedrooms to have a distinctive brand in their area.

   (a) Explain **one** reason why it is important for Guy's Bedrooms to create a distinctive brand.

                                                        (2 marks)

        ....

        ....

   (b) Describe **two** ways that Emma and Steven could establish and differentiate their brand.

                                                        (4 marks)

    1   ....

        ....

    2   ....

        ....

11 There are many factors that affect Guy's Bedrooms marketing strategy.

   (a) Give **two** factors that were important when Emma and Steven chose their physical location.

                                                          (2 marks)

        ....

        ....

   Guy's Bedrooms operates a cost plus pricing strategy but Emma and Steven are aware that there
   are alternative pricing strategies they could use.

   (b) Explain **one** advantage and **one** disadvantage of the cost plus pricing strategy.   **(4 marks)**

   Advantage: ....

        ....

   Disadvantage: ....

        ....

   (c) Describe **one** alternative pricing strategy they could use.   **(2 marks)**

        ....

        ....

   (d) The business has recently extended its product portfolio to include a new range of modern
       wardrobes with sliding doors. Give **two** reasons why it is important for Guy's Bedrooms to
       offer a range of products to its customers.   **(2 marks)**

    1   ....

    2   ....

12 Steven wants to review their marketing mix to check it is still effective. He would like to attract more first-time house buyers. They are younger than his usual target market and he knows that their buying habits are different. Research has told him that most people will soon have smartphones and online shopping is on the increase. He cannot see, though, how he can sell fitted wardrobes online.

Discuss changes Steven could make to each of his 4 Ps that would enable him to attract younger customers. **(8 marks)**

....

....

....

....

....

....

....

....

....

....

....

....

....

....

....

....

....

....

....

....

....

....

....

....

....

....

Answers

LEARNING AIM A

1. Start-up costs

1 **B** A pressure washer **D** Overalls for the staff

2 Any three from: deposit on rent for the premises; charges for fitting the barn out with kennels and runs; feeding bowls/dog leads and other dog care items; advertising; insurance.

3 Claire will have to fit out the premises she finds with a counter, oven and electronic till so that she can operate her business. She will need money to advertise so that customers are aware it has opened.

2. Operating (running) costs

1 Start-up costs: sewing machine; shelves/rails for storing stock.

Running costs: thread; electricity.

2 Any three from: staff wages; petrol/diesel; car servicing; rent on premises; utilities (gas, electricity, water, phone).

3 (a) **A** Buying items to resell **D** Paying his brother to help out on a Saturday

(b) Running costs are the costs that occur again and again when you are operating a business.

3. Fixed and variable costs

1 (a) Any four from: machine maintenance costs; telephone charges; utilities (gas, electricity, water, phone); interest on loan repayment; monthly repayment of loan; business rates; insurance.

(b) Wood and other materials used in manufacture, such as paint, varnish and glue, and postage costs for toys sold.

2 (a) Rent is usually a **fixed** cost because it does not **change** regardless of the level of activity or the number of items made and sold.

(b) Postage and packing costs are often **variable** costs because the cost **increases** with the level of activity or as more items are made, sold and despatched.

4. Calculating total costs

1 (a) Variable costs = **Cost of one unit** × Number of units produced

(b) £5 × 50 = £250

2 Total costs = **Fixed costs + Variable costs**

3 (a) Variable costs = £10 × 100 = £1,000

(b) Fixed cost = £400

(c) Variable costs = £10 × 200
= £2,000
+ Fixed costs = £400
Total costs = £2,400

5. Sources of revenue

1 Any four from: sales revenues from selling bikes; repairing bikes; selling advertising space; rent from the spare room; interest from his savings account.

2 Any two from: selling sportswear and trainers; selling snacks; selling energy drinks; day memberships; spa treatments; special fitness classes; offering physiotherapy; a children's crèche (any other suitable answers are fine).

3 **B** Selling wild bird food **D** Offering plant food and weedkiller for sale

6. Calculating revenue

1 Revenue = **Number of sales × Price per unit**

2 (a) 300 × £30 = £9,000 per month

(b) £9,000 × 12 = £108,000

3 Total revenue = 200 × £1.00 = £200
300 × £1.50 = £450
= £200 + £450 = £650

7. Types of expenditure

1 **A** Buying cards to sell **C** Wages for an assistant

2 Two from: rent; business rates; electricity; machine maintenance; staff wages; key blanks and other stock items.

3 Overheads are the everyday running costs of a business.

8. Understanding and calculating profit or loss

1 Profit = **Revenue** − Expenditure

2 Profit/loss = £30,000 − £25,000 = £5,000.
Ken made a profit.

3 It can increase revenue. This means it will earn more from sales or other sources. It can reduce expenditure. This means it will spend less on running the business. These actions will help it to increase profits because revenue and expenditure are both used to calculate profit. The greater the revenue received and the lower the expenditure, the higher the profit that is left.

LEARNING AIM B

9. Break-even charts

1 The purpose of a break-even chart is to demonstrate how many units have to be produced and sold before the business begins to make a profit.

2

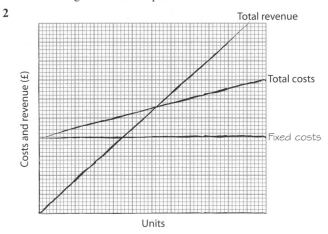

3 Fixed costs and variable costs

10. Interpreting break-even charts

1 (a) and (b)

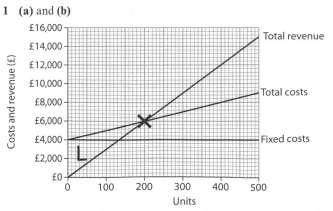

2 **(a)** The fixed costs amount is £4,000.

(b) The total cost for 400 units is £8,000.

(c) The total revenue for 300 units is £9,000.

3 **(a)** The profit area shows how much profit would be made for a given number of sales.

(b) The margin of safety shows how much sales would have to fall by before the break-even point is reached.

11. Using the breakeven formula to calculate the break-even point

1

Furniture items	Fixed costs (£)	Selling price per unit (£)	Variable cost per unit (£)	Break-even point
Item 1	1,000	50	30	**50**
Item 2	300	25	10	**20**
Item 3	7,000	100	30	**100**

2 **(a)** Breakeven is 100 stair gates per week.

(b) The new break-even point is 150 stair gates.

12. The value of breakeven analysis and the risks of ignoring it

1 **A** The total costs are calculated **C** The effect of changes in raw material prices can be assessed

2 Breakeven analysis will allow Nadia to identify how many items she must sell to make a profit, based on the total costs of production and the selling price. It will show if her problem is caused by not selling enough, or whether her costs are too high, for each product in her range.

Nadia can then decide whether to reduce the costs of items that are not profitable, or increase the selling price. If some items are making a bigger loss than others she might want to discontinue those, especially if some items in her range are making a profit. However, breakeven analysis will not show the overall profit Nadia's company will make, so she needs to complete the analysis for every item in her range to identify which is causing an issue.

If Nadia decides to reduce her costs for items to make them profitable she may reduce her fixed costs. This would also reduce the break-even point for items that are already profitable, increasing her overall profitability. She may then be able to increase the selling price of these items to increase her revenue further.

13. The effect of changes on the break-even point

1 **A** The break-even point would decrease.

B The break-even point would decrease.

C The break-even point would increase.

2 A business should carry out a breakeven analysis every three months because costs could change. Sales could fall. The business may want to lower the price for a short time to boost sales.

3 **(a)** The break-even point would increase.

(b) Any two from: Martin could increase the selling price and hope that the business does not lose too many customers. He could look for cheaper sources of materials. He could try to use fewer materials. He could try to find different materials that are cheaper.

14. The purpose of budgeting

1 Revenue budget: money from alterations; income from fashion accessories.

Expenditure budget: staff wages; electricity charges.

2 The purpose of setting a revenue budget is to set targets for income from sales. This provides a focus for everyone involved in sales in the business.

3 The purpose of setting an expenditure budget is to set limits on the amount spent on different items. This ensures that the money spent will not exceed targets and will be less than revenue, so the business will make a profit.

15. Budgeting and budgetary control

1 **B** To ensure performance is checked against the agreed plan

2 Allowing an overspend in budgets, because of a lack of budgetary control, means that the business could be **making a loss**.

3 Department B has overspent by £1,000. This needs investigation.

16. Cash flow forecasting

1 The purpose of a cash flow forecast is to identify the money that should be coming into a business and the money that should be going out of a business.

2 Inflows: interest on savings account; sales revenue. Outflows: purchase of raw materials; insurance.

3 **(a)** The level of cash in the business.

(b) The forecast enables the owner to spot if the level of cash is too low in advance. This will allow the owner to take action before any problems occur.

17. Calculating net inflows/outflows

1 **A** Total inflows, total outflows and opening bank balance

2 **(a)** Closing balance = £5,000

(b) (£1,000)

3

	June (£)
Total receipts	£60,000
Total payments	£50,000
Net inflows/outflows	**£10,000**
Opening balance	£13,000
Closing balance	**£23,000**

18. Impact of timings on cash flow

1 In a cash transaction the buyer pays immediately. In a credit transaction the buyer is allowed a certain amount of time before payment is due.

2 **(a)** Two from: sending out invoices promptly; sending out reminders or phoning to chase up payments; offering discounts for prompt payment; not giving credit to unknown customers.

(b) This would reduce her outflows on a temporary basis so that she would have a higher net cash flow that month. However, her suppliers may threaten not to supply her in future unless she pays them as agreed. If word gets around, she could find it difficult to get suppliers to trade with her at all.

3 **(a)** Business B is the ice-cream van as net cash flow was highest during the summer months when ice cream is most popular.

(b) The ice-cream van is a seasonal business so its cash flow varies. However, as it still has some bills to pay all year round then it is likely to have more problems than the sweet shop, where trade is fairly constant.

(c) Any one from: saving money from the summer months; reduce stock levels in the winter; employ seasonal staff; start selling ice cream elsewhere, such as in a shop.

19. The benefits of using a cash flow forecast and the risks of not doing it

1 Marcus may have to pay for urgent car repairs and if he does not keep his vehicles repaired and in good condition he will lose business. He will also need to replace his vehicles regularly with new models and needs money to pay for this.

2 (a) Delayed payments will reduce Marcus's revenue for the month. This could create difficulties when he has to pay his own bills.

   (b) Family trade is seasonal and dependent on the weather. So, although they pay cash, which is good for his cash flow, during some months he will make less money from them.

3 If Marcus doesn't do this then he will not be able to identify the timing of his inflows and outflows. This means that some business customers may owe him money but he may not be aware and so will miss out on important revenue. Also, it means that he might not realise an urgent bill is due or be unable to pay it.

   Marcus would be unable to plan for the future. If he forecasted he could see when problems might be happening and take action ahead of time to deal with these. For example, he couldn't plan when best to repair his cars and might have to borrow money to do so, which would be expensive. He also wouldn't be able to take advantage of any surplus money that he did have and invest it to gain interest.

   If businesses continued to not pay Marcus and if he was unable to plan when best to use his money then he could run out of money and have to cease trading.

20. Completing and analysing cash flow forecasts

1 **C** It shows how much money the business will have

2

	January (£)	February (£)	March (£)
Total receipts	16,250	10,600	12,550
Total payments	12,100	12,400	10,800
Net inflow/outflow	**4,150**	**(1,800)**	**1,750**
Opening balance	18,150	**22,300**	**20,500**
Closing balance	**22,300**	**20,500**	**22,250**

3 (a) Abigail has a net outflow in November of £12,000 which makes her opening balance negative for both December and January. The bank will charge her money on this overdraft and she could have problems paying her own bills. It is only at the end of January that she has a positive bank balance again. Abigail should try to avoid this situation by planning more carefully so that her payments do not exceed her receipts as much as they did in November.

   (b) The best month would be February when she will start with a positive opening balance of £13,000.

LEARNING AIM C

21. Cost of sales

1 **C** The price paid for items used to make a product

2 Flour and icing sugar

3 **C** £20,000

22. Gross profit

1 (a) Gross profit is the money made from selling a product after the cost of producing it has been deducted.

   (b) Gross profit = **Revenue − Cost of sales**

2

Total sales revenue	**£1,200**
Total cost of sales	**£300**
Gross profit	**£900**

3 Option A = £1,500 − £500 = £1,000
   Option B = £1,600 − £400 = £1,200

23. The impact of positive and negative gross profit

1 There is a positive gross profit figure when **revenue** is greater than the **cost of sales**.

   The gross profit figure is negative when the **cost of sales** is greater than **revenue**.

2 (a) Revenue = £2.00 × 500 = £1,000
       Cost of sales = £0.75 × 500 = £375
       Gross profit = £1,000 − £375 = £625

   (b) £750 − £1,200 = (£450)

   (c) Any two from: he will be able to pay his expenses; he may have enough money for better equipment or expansion; he knows sufficient goods are being sold to produce a profit; he knows his cost of sales is about right.

3 Any two from: reduce the price she pays for cost of sale items, such as bread, butter and sandwich fillings; try to obtain the items from cheaper suppliers; try to promote her café to obtain more sales; increase the selling price of some of the items she sells to increase her sales revenue.

24. Net profit

1 Net profit = **Gross profit − Expenditure**

2 £700 − £250 = £450 (the information on income from sales and cost of ingredients is not needed to calculate net profit as they were already used to calculate gross profit)

3 Gross profit: £6,000 − £2,000 = £4,000
   Net profit: £4,000 − £3,000 = £1,000

4 It is not a good decision because gross profit still has other expenses that have to be deducted before arriving at the final net (actual) profit figure, so he does not actually have £18,000 to spend. Simon's business could be improved by reinvesting any remaining profit into the business so that he can afford the car in future years without impacting on the business' growth.

25. The impact of positive and negative net profit

1 (a) Year 1 as Sam's net profit is a positive figure.

   (b) He has just made a negative net profit of £6,000.

   (c) He can reduce his expenditure which has increased by £11,000 in a year.

   (d) Sam will run out of money and will not have enough to pay his staff wages or his bills. Eventually he will have to crease trading.

2 **D** Total costs are higher than sales revenue

3 Any two from: the business can buy new or better equipment; it has the money to expand; it can employ more staff; it can make or sell more products; the owner can take some for his/her personal use; staff can be paid a bonus.

26. Financial statements

1 (a) **D** Statement of financial position

   (b) Assets: items that a business buys that normally last a long time, such as a van or a computer.
       Liabilities: amounts of money which a business owes.

2

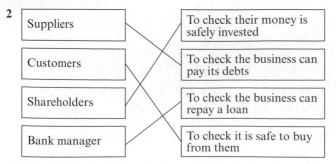

3 To check its financial activities; to check whether it has made a profit or loss; because it is required by law.

27. Income statement (profit and loss account)

1 The purpose of an income statement is to show the business owner the amount of gross and net profit that has been made by the business.

2 (a) The first three lines are the trading account.

(b) Gross profit: £50,000 − £15,000 = £35,000
Net profit: £35,000 − £23,000 = £12,000

	£	£
Income from sales		50,000
Cost of sales	15,000	
Gross profit		**35,000**
Expenses		
Wages and salaries	20,000	
Utilities	3,000	
Net profit		**12,000**

3

	£	£
Income from sales		**20,000**
Cost of sales	5,000	
Gross profit		**15,000**
Expenses		
Wages and salaries	8,000	
Utilities	2,000	
Net profit		**5,000**

28. Assets, liabilities and working capital

1 Computer; van

2 An overdraft is a current liability because it is a debt that has to be repaid soon.

3 (a)

	£
Current assets	6,000
Current liabilities	2,000
Working capital	4,000

(b) All businesses need money to operate. They have to buy stock and pay their own bills. Without working capital they cannot do this.

29. The statement of financial position (balance sheet)

1 **B** A snapshot of a business' finances at a particular point in time

D A summary of the money invested in a business and what it has been spent on

2 (a) Stock, trade receivables and cash in bank are all 'current assets' because they are constantly changing as stock is sold and money is received or credit is given to buyers.

(b) Duncan needs to send reminders so that they will pay more promptly.

(c) £10,000 was invested originally and then £7,000 of profits was retained.

(d) The business is financially sound because its working capital is £7,000. This means that even if Duncan paid all his debts he would still have £7,000 in assets that he could turn into cash if he needed to.

30. Completing a statement of financial position (balance sheet)

1 Trade payables are debts owed by the business and are a liability.

2

ASSETS	£	£
Fixed assets		
Equipment/machines		**12,000**
Current assets		
Stock	2,500	
Trade receivables	2,100	
Cash in bank	3,000	7,600
Total assets		**19,600**
LIABILITIES		
Current liabilities		
Trade payables	1,600	
Overdraft	1,000	2,600
Working capital (net current assets)		**5,000**

3

ASSETS	£	£
Fixed assets		
Equipment/machines		**12,000**
Van		**1,500**
Current assets		
Stock	2,500	
Trade receivables	2,100	
Cash in bank	1,000	5,600
Total assets		**19,100**
LIABILITIES		
Current liabilities		
Trade payables	1,100	
Overdraft	1,000	2,100
Working capital (net current assets)		**3,500**

31. Increasing profits and analysing an income statement (profit and loss account)

1 **B** Negotiating cheaper rates for buying paper
D Increasing his prices

2 (a) Gross profit = £175,000 − £67,000 = £108,000

(b) Net profit = £108,000 − £83,000 = £25,000

(c) Her advertising costs are high. As she has an internet connection she could do more electronic marketing which is cheaper and reduce her advertising bill.

Her wage bill also seems high. She could perhaps reduce this by employing temporary or part-time staff just to cover busy times.

3 Increasing prices would result in increased sales revenue which would boost gross profits. However, if this meant fewer sales because customers bought from competitors instead, then revenue may fall and profits would fall too.

32. Analysing a statement of financial position (balance sheet) for a small business

1 Rob's working capital is negative. It means that he has not got enough money to operate the business and cannot meet his debts. He needs to get money from his trade receivables as soon as possible. Also, Rob only has £400 cash in bank which is not enough to pay for his day-to-day expenses. He should sell some stock to increase this figure so that this amount becomes positive.

To improve his working capital Rob should also reduce his current liabilities. He should look closely at the amount of money he owes to his suppliers, his trade payables. At the moment it is too high and if they all demanded payment he would not be able to pay. He needs to start paying them back as soon as possible to improve his working capital. He should try to negotiate part-payments or obtain an extension to the credit period.

Rob has spent most of the £3,000 he borrowed through his overdraft. He should plan to repay it as soon as he can to avoid the interest that the bank will charge him. If he improves his current liabilities, then his working capital will improve.

2 Some customers may fail to pay if they are not reminded or even go out of business themselves, so Rob would not get the money he is owed. He should chase up these customers to reduce this amount as quickly as possible.

33. Exam skills 1

1 **B** Road tax for van

2 **A** Computer equipment **C** Production machinery

3 **B** Staff wages **D** Purchase of raw materials

4 **A** Sales revenue **C** Cost of sales

34. Exam skills 2

1 (a) 1,500   (b) 2,000

2 200 × £11 = £2,200

3

	£
Sales revenue	10,000
Cost of sales	2,000
Gross profit	**8,000**
Expenses	5,000
Net profit	**3,000**

35. Exam skills 3

1 (a)

	£
Total receipts	**5,000**
Total payments	**3,500**
Net inflow/outflow	**1,500**
Opening balance	**16,000**
Closing balance	**17,500**

(b) Building an extension would mean that he can attract and serve more customers, which will increase his receipts and profits in the future.

2 (a) Although Liam's sales are high, his cost of sales are also high, which means he only has a low gross profit. His expenditure is even higher, meaning that he has a negative net profit.

(b) Increase his gross profit by buying cheaper materials so that his cost of sales is lower. Increase his gross profit by raising his selling price to increase his sales revenue. Increase his net profit by reducing his expenditure.

UNIT 9 ANSWERS

LEARNING AIM A

36. Defining marketing and its importance to business

1 Marketing involves identifying and understanding customer needs and expectations and providing products or services to meet their needs profitably.

2 Market share is the percentage of the total sales of a product accounted for by one business.

3 1 Through effective marketing they will identify the best products that their customers will want to buy, such as the best ice-cream flavours, the food they will want to eat in the tea room and any goods that are sold on the premises. This should ensure that sales are good.

 2 Through effective marketing they can promote their tea room so that potential customers know about them and will want to visit. Because the products on offer are those that customers want to buy, this will also encourage customer loyalty and repeat business.

37. How businesses use marketing

1 Two of the following: to boost flagging sales; to penetrate new markets; to promote the brand; to maintain customer loyalty.

2 Competitive advantage is the advantage gained over competitors from offering superior or more attractive products or services.

3 (a) The benefit to Chillax of identifying customer needs is that they can then design products that meet these needs and it will not end up producing a range that no one wants.

 (b) The benefit to Chillax of investigating competitor products is that they can check what is already on the market and how much competitor products cost. They can then aim to produce something better.

 (c) Simply reducing prices will lower profits if sales levels do not increase. Chillax has therefore chosen to add more value for customers by producing a high end range which gives the customers the design and appearance they want. This better meets customer needs so sales should increase, leading to greater profitability.

38. Marketing, corporate objectives and SMART objectives

1 The marketing plan will link to the corprate objectives, such as planning to open more outlets, that need to be undertaken to enable Max to expand The Chocolate Experience.

2

	Meaning of letter	Definition
S =	Specific	Objectives state an exact numerical target
M =	Measurable	Objectives are easily measured
A =	Achievable	Objectives can be achieved with the resources available
R =	Realistic	Objectives are possible for that business
T =	Time-based	Objectives have a deadline date for achievement

3 (a) A corporate objective is an aim the business wants to achieve.

 (b) One of the following: to increase profits; to increase sales; to enter new markets; to introduce new products; to update existing products; to increase market share; (or any other acceptable business aim).

(c) To open two new outlets in the next 12 months (or any other specific, reasonable number plus a sensible deadline date). (More than four new outlets would not be realistic because even two new outlets would mean doubling the size of the business.)

39. B2B and B2C markets

1 The B2C market means the business to consumer market. This means that the business sells to private individuals and households.

2 Any two from:
She will:
- carry out market research to understand the needs of her customers
- have a memorable shop/brand name
- advertise in the local press.

She may also:
- have a database of customers and send them email newsletters or information on new trends
- run promotions and give special offers at certain times of the year.

3 **(a)** The B2B market means the business to business market. This means selling to other businesses or retailers.

(b) Any two from:
- seeing examples of Shazia's past work and her proposals for their hotel
- a competitive price for the work with credit terms for payments
- good-quality work with good after-sales support
- prompt delivery on specific dates agreed in advance
- Shazia's style ideas in terms of linking to the style of the hotel
- examples of her experience and expertise that they can rely on.

40. Other types of markets

1 **(a)** Bartletts operates in the goods market.

(b) Little Feet operates in the goods market because it sells shoes. It also operates in the services market because it provides a service to parents by measuring children's feet accurately.

2 The special equipment in the factory is a capital good. The trainers are a consumer good.

3 **(a)** The parents are the customers and they will make the decision on whether or not to purchase the trainers. The decision will depend on factors such as fit and price rather than appearance or flashing lights.

(b) Little Feet operates in a niche market because the mass market would be for shoes in general and Little Feet focuses just on children's trainers.

41. Business models

1 A business model is the way in which a business makes money or adds value to the business – for example, by selling goods or advertising.

2 Jack Flash Motors operates a sales model because the focus is on selling the cars that Jack has bought. These are priced cheaply to encourage customers to buy in a basic 'no-frills' environment.

3 **(a)** Ryan operates a marketing model because he focuses on the needs of individual clients.

(b) Ryan will gain customer loyalty because he will advise them on updates to the website and implement these to keep the content updated. This will result in repeat business, and satisfied clients may recommend him to people they know. This will help him to increase the number of clients he has.

42. Business orientation and choice of business model

1 **(a)** Brian's business is product orientated.

(b) Sue's business is market orientated.

2 **(a)** Brian operates a sales model because he grows the plants he wants to grow and then sells them.

(b) Brian's products are more specialised and will only appeal to a niche market. Potential customers may not live locally. Therefore, he needs to target people further away which is where a website will help his business. He can appeal to a wider audience and his reputation as an expert will mean people will buy from him.

3 **(a)** Sue operates a marketing model because she aims to meet the needs of local people.

(b) Sue is keen to supply what local people want and in the quantities they want them. She also listens to what they want and responds to their requests. This will mean she gains a loyal customer base as she will provide them with a personal service that they may not get in larger outlets or from online providers.

43. Branding – its importance and dimensions

1 The term brand dimensions means the components that make up a distinctive brand. For example, the logo, images and the colours that represent the brand and its values.

2 Any two from:
Whippersnappers can:
- create a distinctive logo that people will associate with their business
- decide on a symbol to represent the business which people will easily recognise and remember
- decide on colours for its logo and for staff uniforms, leaflets and other publicity materials that are different from those of its competitors
- have images that show children having fun with the Whippersnappers name and the staff in their uniforms shown in the images
- have a celebrity endorsement that it could use in its advertising.

3 **(a)** Brand consistency is important because all the dimensions of the brand need to give the same message about the brand.

(b) Brand values are the standards that a business prides itself on. Whippersnappers wants to show that children can come to have fun and be safe as adults can watch them at all times. Its images and publicity materials should therefore show this.

44. The benefits of building brands

1 Three of the following:
- She is more likely to get repeat purchases because customers trust branded products
- It adds value because customers are more willing to try new products if they are branded
- She can probably charge a higher price than if the product was unbranded, which will help Marian to expand the business and increase her profits
- It will make Granny's Garden products stand out from those of its competitors, which will help to increase sales and market share.

2 (a) An appropriate brand personality will help people to see the brand in a certain way and they will feel it has certain characteristics. This will help sales.

(b) The name of Marian's brand has a homely feel and introduces the idea of fresh produce. Marian's brand personality could use this idea and concentrate on how her business uses good, healthy, fresh produce, which has been prepared in a traditional way, without additives or flavourings.

3 Marian could extend her brand. Brand extension means adding other related or adapted products, such as pickles or jams, to her range. As people will already know her brand, her regular customers will want to try her new products too.

LEARNING AIM B

45. Market research – types and sources of data

1 Market research is gathering information about customers, competitors and markets by collecting primary and secondary data. This is then used to make marketing decisions.

2 (a) This data is quantitative data because it relates to numbers. In this example, it relates to the number of places in the Lake District that allow visitors to bring their dogs.

(b) It is secondary data because it is information which already exists at the tourist information office.

3 (a) This is qualitative data because it involves people's views and opinions.

(b) It is primary data because it is original. It does not exist until Jacqui obtains it from potential customers.

(c) Jacqui could create a questionnaire and then ask tourists to the area, especially those with a dog, to complete it.

46. The uses of data to support marketing activity

1 Jacqui has not found any evidence to support her idea of a pet café. Local people have shown little interest in the idea and most visitors leave their dogs at home.

2 More and more cafés have outdoor eating areas.
The number of tourists holidaying in the area is increasing. More people are coming on short breaks or day trips.

3 (a) A gap in the market means that there is a customer need which is not being fully met at the moment.

(b) Jacqui can benefit because she is looking for an opportunity to start her own business. There is little holiday accommodation that allows pets, which is the gap in the market. By identifying this gap in the market she knows that if she starts holiday accommodation where pet owners are welcome, there should be a market for it.

47. The uses of internal and external data and situational analysis

1 (a) Benchmarking means obtaining data that will enable a business to compare itself with its competitors on certain characteristics.

(b) Two of the following: information on their facilities; the range of animals they have; their prices; their opening hours; the size of their premises; their ease of access and car parking.

(Any other comparative information on a farm which operates as a visitor attraction is acceptable.)

2 (a) Situational analysis is when a business looks at its own position in the market and assesses how it could be affected by trends and developments.

(b) Weaknesses; Opportunities; Threats.

(c) One of the following:
- Jacqui can check that she has sufficient strengths for the business to stand a chance of success.
- Jacqui can identify any weaknesses to see if these can be remedied before she goes any further.
- She can identify further opportunities that will enable her to strengthen her idea.
- She can identify any threats and decide if these are serious enough to stop her going any further with her plans.

48. The purpose of market research and analysis

1 (a) The target market is the target customer or section of the market that the business aims to supply.
(The aim is to find a gap in the market, in terms of what is currently offered to these customers, and fill it.)

(b) Two of the following:
They will:
- understand what facilities their target customers want
- know how much they are prepared to pay
- know what appeals to them and what does not
- know how to promote the attraction to gain attention and custom
- know what potential customers dislike and want to avoid.

2 Any one from:
- They will identify their main competitors.
- They will find out the key characteristics of competitors and why they appeal to customers.
- They will be able to analyse the strengths and weaknesses of their competitors.
- They will be able to identify something that they can offer that their competitors cannot.

3 Any two from:
- Market trends will enable her to identify the size and value of the market in her area, which will enable her to work out whether she can make a profit in this market.
- Market trends will show whether the market is growing or declining (and how quickly). She stands less chance of success if the demand for visitor attractions is declining.
- Market trends will identify the level of competition. If this is intense then she may struggle to survive. If there are many competitors then she may stand little chance of attracting much business.

49. Interpreting key market research findings

1 Market growth means the market is worth more each year.

2 (a) A niche market is a small, focused market (or group of customers) that concentrates on a specialised product.

(b) Two of the following: the number of farm shops is increasing; over 50 per cent of people prefer to buy local food; over 50 per cent of people trust the quality of local food; the number of people who prefer to buy local food is increasing.

3 Any two from:
- It can focus on specialist products, such as meat from its rare breed of pigs, and charge premium prices.
- It will not be in direct competition with supermarkets.
- It can advertise and promote products to its target market.
- It can keep expenses down as it will not be hoping to expand and open other branches.

50. PESTLE analysis

1 Economic; Social; Legal

2 Political – the government is supportive of farm shops and provides help and advice.

Economic – the economy is picking up so people have more money to spend at the moment.

Social – people are holidaying in the UK and are buying more fresh food. Shoppers trust local suppliers more than supermarkets.

Technology – more people are shopping online.

Legal – they may need planning permission for converting their barn to a shop.

Environmental – farm shops use less packaging and reduce food miles.

3 Possible answers to support the idea:

- Support and advice on setting up and running farm shops is available on government websites.
- The economy is picking up and so is consumer spending.
- Market research has shown that more people are buying from farm shops and prefer fresh food.
- Current trends show that more people are holidaying in the UK.
- They could sell food online and provide vegetable boxes for local people so they are not totally dependent on visitors.

Possible answers against the idea:

- Fuel prices are high which may prevent people visiting.
- Consumer spending may fall if the economy goes into another recession.
- If the economy continues to recover then people may start holidaying abroad again.
- Planning permission may be difficult to get and costly.

Your conclusion should be based on your evidence.
You may conclude that because most factors are positive then, unless there are a lot of other farm shops in the area, they should stand a good chance of success if they plan carefully.

LEARNING AIM C

51. The marketing mix – an overview

1 The marketing mix is a combination of factors that help a business to sell its products successfully to its target customer.

2 Price; Promotion.

3 Asiya and Bethany must consider all aspects of the marketing mix. This will help them focus on the needs of their target customers. Under 'product' they must assess the look of the product, the taste, the packaging and the brand name to see if these will appeal to their target customers. They will have to identify the best price for the biscuits, the places to sell them – where their target customer will find them – and how to promote the product so that their target customers know it exists.

52. Product differentiation

1 (a) USP stands for unique selling point. It is the particular characteristic that makes a product different from others on the market.

(b) Choca2 chocolate biscuits are flavoured with cardamom.

2 1 They could package them so that they look attractive and appealing in small transparent bags with bows and an informative label.

2 They could offer gift boxes which include a leaflet containing information about cardamom and some recipes using it.

3 There are many types of biscuits on the market. As these are special spiced biscuits it is important to make customers aware of this difference through the name, the packaging and a description on the packets. This will make them instantly noticeable for customers looking for something different.

53. Product life cycle

1 Growth; Decline

2 (a) Development/Introduction.

(b) Two of the following: sales are growing slowly; customers are trying the product; profits are low.

3 (a) An extension strategy is a method of extending the life of a product.

(b) Two of the following: they could introduce new flavours; they could change their packaging; they could advertise to a new target market; they could launch the biscuits in new markets, e.g. overseas.

54. Product portfolios

1 A product portfolio is the range of products produced or sold by a business.

2 Any two from: it will need to check which products are selling well and which are not; it may have to decide which new products to make; it needs to decide when to withdraw a product that isn't selling; it will want to increase sales if a product is not selling well; it has to identify when to launch a new product.

3 Asiya's idea has several advantages. Keeping the product portfolio small will mean that they will spend less money on developing new products, that they will need less space for storage of various ingredients and bakeware and that they can focus on the products they know well and that their customers will associate with their brand. There are also several drawbacks with keeping the portfolio very narrow. The disadvantages of a small portfolio are that the business is dependent on one product being successful. Having a broader portfolio will help them to spread risk – if the biscuit sales fall then other products may still sell well. A small portfolio may only appeal to a niche market, whereas a broader portfolio will appeal to a wider market and attract new customers, which should increase their overall revenue. If they have a broader portfolio where all the products include oriental spices then they will benefit from the same USP for their whole brand.

55. Pricing strategies

1 A pricing strategy is the method used to decide what price to charge. This will depend on the type of product and the level of competition.

2 Mark up pricing; premium pricing; penetration pricing; competitive pricing.

3 Any two from:

- Premium pricing would mean that they maximise their revenue because prices are high and customers will associate their brand with luxury. The disadvantage is that sales may be low if customers think the biscuits are too expensive.
- Mark up pricing would mean that they are certain they cover their costs and make a profit but the price set may be less than customers are prepared to pay so they could lose money.

- Penetration pricing would attract people because the biscuits would be cheap and sales may be high. The problem is that people may think that the biscuits are poor quality and may be discouraged. Revenue would also be less than if the price was higher.

- Competitive pricing would mean that customers are likely to consider the price good compared with competitor products so sales should be good. A disadvantage is that they would not be getting a premium price for the fact that their product is different and not mass produced.

56. Elasticity of demand

1 Price elasticity of demand relates to the fact that demand for most goods usually falls when prices rise and vice versa.

2 If demand for the biscuits is elastic then demand will fall by more than the increase in price.

3 (a) 2/10 = 0.2

(b) This shows demand is inelastic as the quantity sold fell by less than the price increase. Within reason, the price could therefore be increased a little more to maximise sales revenue.

57. Place – distribution channels

1 Distribution channels are the methods used to get the products from the producer to the consumer. This will depend on the type of product and the buying habits of the target customer.

2 Any three from: online to the customer directly from its website; from their own stall at local markets; from a factory shop; from their own retail shops; through Choca2 parties.

3 If Choca2 sells directly to customers then it has the benefit of controlling the way the biscuits are promoted and sold and can set the price paid by the customer. The disadvantages are that there will be extra costs related to running a shop or selling online and posting biscuits – which could get damaged – to online customers.

An advantage of selling to the farm shop is that these costs would be avoided and Asiya and Bethany could concentrate on just producing the biscuits. They are likely to sell the biscuits in larger quantities but would have to sell to the farm shop at a discount price for the farm shop to make a profit. The customer would probably pay more because the retailers would add on a percentage to make a profit. But Asiya and Bethany are unsure whether they could produce the quantities required and they may have no influence on where the products are situated in the shop or how they are promoted. If sales are low, the farm shop may cancel the order.

58. Place – business location

1 Any three from: their production facility will need to be near to suppliers because they willl need to buy ingredients; they will need good transport links; the price of land/premises will be an important factor; the availability of labour to work in the factory may be important.

2 Any two from: they need to be near to customers to be able to attract passing trade; the price of premises is important; they may benefit from being near competitors, such as in a shopping mall or on the high street.

3 Two of the following: they will need good telecommunications – specifically a reliable high-speed broadband link; they also need good transport to distribute the goods to customers; they need to be near to a transport firm or post office so that it is easy to post goods or arrange for them to be collected.

59. The promotional mix, budget and channels

1 The promotional mix is the combination of promotional methods chosen to advertise and promote a product or brand.

2 The business will want to spend some money on advertising and promotions but it must not spend more than it can afford. Having a budget means that some money is set aside for this and spending is monitored to prevent overspending.

3 Any three from: sales promotions, such as competitions, point-of-sale materials or free gifts will attract shoppers and encourage them to buy; public relations and publicity, such as getting the local paper to feature them in an article, will cost nothing and make people more aware of their brand; direct marketing, such as sending out mailshots or emailing newsletters, can be done if Choca2 has a database of customers they have supplied previously; personal selling at food fairs or visiting shops to ask them to stock their biscuits would increase sales; emarketing, such as advertising on their own website or using social media, would also be a cost-effective way of promoting their brand.

60. Viral marketing and guerrilla advertising

1 The term social media means websites, blogs and other online platforms that allow individuals to post and share information.

2 Any two from:

- Having a Facebook page means that customers can 'like' and share information with their friends.

- Having a Twitter feed means that they can tweet about new developments under an appropriate hashtag like #spicybiscuits and Twitter users who like the tweet can forward it to their followers.

- Posting a film on YouTube that people watch and forward to their email contacts or post on Facebook would also be a method of getting information spread online.

(Any other type of social media that you can describe accurately in relation to how information could be shared and spread would be acceptable.)

3 Guerrilla marketing using a flash mob is usually a very cheap way of getting publicity. If people film it and post it online then it can go viral. The press may also be interested. If they are at the event or are sent a photograph then this can gain free publicity.

The disadvantage is that if anything goes wrong then any resultant bad publicity may harm the brand – for example, if the flash mob got out of hand or if there was any dispute with the trade shows organisers. The flash mob may not provide a strong link to the brand. People may remember seeing the flash mob but it is important that it is relevant so people remember Choca2.

Therefore, unless the flash mob is very carefully organised and is done with the permission of the organisers of the fair, it might be wiser for a small business like Choca2 to stick to more conventional forms of promotion.

61. Consistency and the marketing mix

1 All elements must be consistent so that they reinforce the brand image in the mind of the customer.

2 Product: the type of raw materials or ingredients used can be basic or luxury (e.g. plastic or leather).
Price: can be very low – such as products in discount stores – or very high – such as luxury brands in department stores.

3   The exclusive department store with a luxury food hall would attract affluent customers. It would set high prices and promote the ranges to appeal to certain customers. The biscuits would be judged on quality ingredients and taste.

Ｔhe supermarket will attract middle-class shoppers who care about what they eat, many of whom will be prepared to pay a little more for good food. The biscuits will be priced at a price that is competitive with other similar items and they will be found in the 'quality biscuit' section. The biscuits would be judged on taste but also on price and value for money.

The discount chain would want to buy the biscuits as cheaply as possible so it could sell them cheaply. Promotions and displays would be basic as most customers would select mainly on price. This would not fit with the brand image of the Choca2 biscuits.

If Choca2 wants to maximise sales it should choose the supermarket as its retailer. The high price the department store would charge may put the biscuits outside of the price range of many potential customers, so Choca2 should not choose this retailer.

62. Ebusiness and ecommerce

1   Ecommerce means selling or buying goods online and it may also include offering customer service online. Ebusiness is the name given to a business in which all its main business functions, such as HR, finance and stock control, are linked by technology. It may also buy and sell goods online too.

2   Any three from: the business can sell goods 24 hours a day; it can offer goods for sale in overseas markets; it is cheaper than having retail premises; the business can process multiple orders; it can sell through mobile sites and apps on smartphones and tablets; it can promote products using social media.

3   Any three from: stock levels update automatically whenever an order is fulfilled; production rates can be changed automatically to take account of stock levels; sales, stock levels and production can be easily checked; can check that invoices have been sent out promptly; can check that payments (in and out) have been made.

63. Influences on the marketing mix

1   (a)   One of each of the following types of issue:
        Economic issues: rising inflation means that cost prices are rising.
        Social issues: there is a trend for low-fat foods and less sugar in foods.
        Environmental issues: there is pressure to reduce packaging. Ideally all packaging should be recyclable.

    (b)   1   The price of the biscuits may need to increase because of higher costs.
          2   The product may need to be adapted to take into account the trend for low-fat and low-sugar products or a different version may need to be launched.
          3   If the packaging is changed, promotions could focus on how the product is environmentally friendly.

2   New technology may help Choca2 to produce its biscuits more quickly and efficiently because new production equipment may be able to increase output without increasing staff levels. This would mean that the cost of making each biscuit would fall and if prices and sales levels remain the same then profits would increase.

64. Evaluating the effectiveness of the marketing mix

1   Many things, such as technology, economic factors and social factors, change over time. These all influence the marketing mix and may mean that what is successful and appropriate one year is less effective the next year.

2   To be SMART the target must be specific, measurable, achievable, realistic and time-based. Asiya and Bethany should check if their target met all these requirements.

3   Product: they could change the recipe or introduce a low-fat or low-sugar version.
    Price: they could see if there is any scope for lowering the price (or not increasing it) if they buy the new equipment.
    Place: they could assess the places that sell their biscuits to see if these are the best outlets. They could consider selling more online themselves.
    Promotion: they could assess the way the biscuits are promoted in stores. Now that they sell biscuits nationally they could consider paid-for advertising on TV or in the press to see if this increases sales.

65. Exam skills 1

1   Any two from:
    - It can be used to identify customer needs so that the business can develop products to match these.
    - It can boost sales and increase profits.
    - It can increase brand awareness.
    - It can be used to launch new products successfully.
    - It can be used to sell into new markets and increase market share.
    - It can be used to encourage customer retention and loyalty.
    - It can be used to build/enhance the reputation of the business.

2   A product-orientated business uses its expertise to develop and produce a product that is innovative and different – such as Google Glass or the Samsung Galaxy Gear.

3   Any three from: to identify a gap in the market; to identify their target market; to identify the activities of competitors; to understand consumer behaviour and motivation, such as their buying behaviour and where they spend their money; to identify market trends.

4   One from the following: TV advertisements; press advertisements; cinema advertisements; radio advertisements; online (paid-for) advertisements.

5   Any two from: technological changes; economic issues; cultural issues; social issues; ethical issues; political issues. (You may also have identified environmental and legal issues that were mentioned in the PESTLE analysis and either of these would also be correct.)

66. Exam skills 2

1   It groups its products into different colour ranges with accent colours.

2   Any two from: it can identify the type of products that they want to buy; it can focus on selling goods at a price that they will pay; it will know where to situate its stores; it will know its customers' buying habits and how much they spend; it will be able to create adverts and promotions to appeal to its target market.

3   Any two from: a logo; the use of different colours; the use of symbols; images to reflect the personality of the brand; celebrity endorsements to promote the brand.

4 Any three from:

- Using social media, like Facebook and/or Twitter, will enable Accent Accessories to spread information about the stores quickly and cheaply to potential customers.
- People who read the Facebook post or tweet on Twitter can share the information with their friends, increasing the number of people who know about the stores.
- Accent Accessories can use social media to show new products and advertise sales promotions.
- Accent Accessories can get valuable customer feedback on its products and customer service from posts and tweets.

5 Two of the following: At the growth stage of the product life cycle sales and profits are increasing because the product has been accepted; there is more competition as new firms enter the market; businesses have to fight for market share so prices will be competitive; businesses need to differentiate their product in some way.

67. Exam skills 3

1 One from the following:

- One economic factor could be that customers have more money to spend because taxes have fallen, wages are rising or unemployment has fallen. This would mean that the business will have increased sales. Accent Accessories may increase its product range and stock some more expensive ranges. It may increase its prices (especially if its own costs are rising).
- Another economic factor could be that customers have less money to spend because taxes have increased, wages are falling or unemployment is rising. To attract customers, Accent Accessories may have to stock cheaper ranges of goods or try to reduce its prices still further. It may have to reduce its own advertising costs by doing more 'below the line' promotions, which will mean it can reduce its prices.

2 (a) Any two from: the price of different premises will vary; it will need to be near its competitors; it will need to attract passing trade.

(b) The benefits to Accent Accessories of having an ecommerce site are that people would be able to place orders and buy goods 24 hours a day, 7 days a week. They will be able to place these orders from any location where they have internet access, including on smartphones and tablets. This means that Accent Accessories will be able to sell goods in areas where it doesn't have a store. It would be able to receive and process more orders.

The disadvantages to Accent Accessories of having an ecommerce site are that its USP is related to colours and the goods might not be displayed as well online. They are also items that people might want to touch and try on, again which they cannot do online. People might also see shopping in the store as a social activity. Selling online could actually cost the business more, especially if it offers free returns and refunds and needs staff to process these.

The conclusion is that if research shows that selling online would mean that Accent Accessories' prices would have to increase across the whole business it may just be better off selling in the stores and keeping its prices low. However, if research shows that its target market is buying more accessories online, it may want to change its mind.

68. Unit 2: Practice assessment test

1 C Staff wages   **E** Rent for the garage

2 Two from the following: stock of goods; fascia for front of shop; fixtures and fittings; new cash register; advertising opening; deposit for rent. (Or any other accurate start-up cost.)

3 C Heating the shop

4 A Delivery boxes   **D** Pizza ingredients

5

	600 items sold
Variable costs	**£4,200**
Fixed costs	**£3,000**
Total costs	**£7,200**

6 B Insurance   **C** Electricity bill

7 £48,000

8 The business can compare its actual expenditure with its planned expenditure and take immediate action if there is a problem and it is overspending.

9 Breakeven occurs when total revenue and total expenditure are the same.

10 (a)

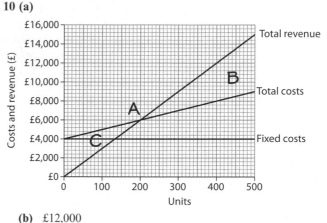

(b) £12,000

11 250

12 A Expenditure

13 (a) To identify how much money will be spent and received and plan how much will be in the bank at the end of each month. The figures should be positive.

(b)

2014	July (£)	August (£)	September (£)
Total receipts	10,000	10,000	**12,000**
Total payments	8,000	10,000	**20,000**
Net inflow/outflow	2,000	0	**(8,000)**
Opening balance	3,200	5,200	**5,200**
Closing balance	5,200	5,200	**(2,800)**

(c) He could take out a bank loan or arrange for an overdraft to ensure that he has enough cash to cover his expenses and continue to run the business.

14 C Buying photographic paper and photo frames

15 A Money owed to suppliers   **C** Bank loan

16 Keiran's cost of sales is too high in relation to his sales – he needs to increase his prices to make a profit or buy from cheaper suppliers. He should try to boost his sales but needs to do this through promotions that are cheap such as email newsletters, not expensive advertisements. His staff wages are high and he may be able to reduce these by cutting staff hours – if someone leaves he should try to cope without replacing them. His postage and packing costs are high in relation to his sales – he should try to negotiate a cheaper rate with a parcel firm.

17

	£	£
Income from sales	82,500	
Cost of sales	25,820	
Gross profit		56,680
Expenses		
Wages and salaries	16,450	
Rent and rates	14,000	
Net profit		26,230

18 Two from the following: she should chase up her debtors to get payments she is owed – her trade receivables figure is too high. She should reduce her overdraft as this is high. She could increase her trade payables by delaying payments to her suppliers for a short time. She could reduce slow moving stock by having a sale.

19 Jason and Kate have planned to make a profit but they need to check they are doing this. First they need to check they have made a gross profit by checking that their revenue is higher than their cost of sales. They must then deduct their expenditure to check their net profit figure. Although they will have to do these calculations at the end of the financial year and prepare an income statement (profit and loss account) and a statement of financial position (balance sheet), they could do this at any time. Preparing an income statement will identify their gross and net profit. If their gross profit is low or negative they need to reduce their cost of sales and/or sell more goods. If their net profit is low they need to identify which areas of expenditure they can reduce.

Their statement of financial position identifies their assets and liabilities. They can see if their debt are too high and if they need to chase up overdue payments. It is important they always have enough working capital or they will not be able to pay wages and their own suppliers. They should also make sure they only borrow money when it is essential as they will then have to pay interest which will add to their costs. If they want to expand or develop the business then they will have to identify ways in which they can obtain capital, such as money from shareholders or by using retained profits.

74. Unit 9: Practice assessment test

SECTION A

1 Marketing means identifying customer needs and meeting these while making a profit. (Any appropriate definition should include a reference to meeting customer needs and making a profit.)

2 Technological

3 B2B stands for Business to Business. This market is made up of businesses that make and supply goods and services for other businesses, for example production equipment or office cleaning.

4 Any of the following: competition will be less fierce as there will be fewer new entrants; the business will have to time to develop slowly rather than cope with rapidly increasing demand; the business can use customer feedback and technological developments to improve its products; prices will be more stable so profits can be accurately forecast; the business can focus on maintaining quality and providing good service.

5 Any one from: when a producer sells to a wholesaler who then sells to the retailer who then sells to the consumer; when a producer sells to a retailer who sells to the consumer; when a producer sells to an agent who sells to the consumer.

6 (a) The advertising model, as most of its revenue comes from advertising.

(b) Any two from: it could ask parents for their opinions about its games and set up a forum on its website for feedback and a discussion group; it could have an online focus group consisting of teachers and parents and ask for their opinions; it could have a consumer panel of children who have used their games and ask them their thoughts on the games; it could issue an online questionnaire for people to complete when they visit the website.

(c) Any two from: market research will tell You Learn Software what its target market thinks about its current games and their features as well as the price it charges; market research will tell You Learn what its competitors are doing and what the current trends in the mobile games market are; market research will tell You Learn about the needs and wants of its customers and their buying behaviour – and it can assess how well it is meeting their needs; market research will identify market trends and show You Learn whether the market is growing and how quickly or slowly.

(d) Arguments in favour of keeping a product orientation are: mobile games are produced by games developers who know the limits they can achieve; many games developers are very creative and may suggest innovative effects and outcomes; the business will employ many talented games developers who enjoy creating new games; many customers will not know what games they want to play until they see them.

Arguments in favour of a marketing orientation are: customers could suggest ideas for an extension strategy (for example, by introducing different levels or new features) which would extend the life of a product; customer ideas could help them to improve existing products, which would increase sales and the projected life of a game; educationalists could help the company to focus on issues that primary schools are focused on and games which included these aspects should sell well; if people were involved in product creation they might be more likely to spread this information using social media and this viral marketing would help increase sales for You Learn Software.

The best option would be for You Learn Software to be more market-focused than in the past so that it can take into account important customer ideas and feedback in the future. This would mean that You Learn would be meeting customer needs better and sales and profits should increase.

SECTION B

7 Above the line:

Any one from: adverts in the press or adverts in Yellow Pages.

Below the line:

Any one from: leaflets through doors; its website, appearing in a home makeover programme on national television; its brochure.

8 Any two from: it can compete with large national firms even though its website and brochure isn't as sophisticated; they will be able to supply customers who cannot buy from national firms because it has odd sized spaces to fill; it can gain a reputation for quality and low prices with local people and receive recommendations; it can offer a range of different, customised products that will gain it customers and enable it to be competitive.

9 It is market orientated because it listens to its customers and adapts what it provides to meet their needs.

10 (a) Guy's Bedrooms needs to create a distinctive brand to differentiate itself from its competitors. It wants to be memorable to customers and to create an image that will stick in people's minds and be attractive to potential customers. This will make it easier for customers to recognise it and understand what it represents – for example, a personal service and value for money.

(b) Any two from: they could design an eye-catching logo or lettering that they have on staff uniforms, their website and their vehicles; they could adopt certain colours that they think represent their brand and use these for their logo, in their brochures and in the design studio; they could use a symbol that would represent their brand; they could ensure that all the images in the brochure reflect the types of stylish bedrooms they can create and include positive customer feedback; they could use any contacts they made while on the home makeover programme to try to get celebrity endorsements of their products and services.

11 (a) Any two from: they would want an area where rents are cheap because they need space for a workshop and a design studio and they want to continue to sell at competitive prices; they would need good transport links as they need it to be easily accessible by road for customers to visit and for their vans to deliver furniture; they would need to be quite near to their target market – if in a remote location few people would visit.

(b) Any one from: an advantage of cost plus pricing is that the business knows that it is covering its costs and is making a profit; an advantage is that it is simple to calculate and can be used by all staff if they know how much profit to add on.

Any one from: a disadvantage is that the business may be asking cheaper prices than customers are prepared to pay; a disadvantage is that it takes no account of the actions of competitors or how much customers can afford to spend. This means the business may be asking more than people are prepared to pay.

(c) Any one from: they could use competitive pricing by checking the price that competitors charge and asking the same or a bit less; they could develop a luxury range and use premium pricing for this range for customers who can afford to spend more.

(d) Any two from: products have different life cycles and some styles of wardrobes and furniture will be out of date and need to be replaced or updated; some products are more successful than others and offering several ranges helps Guy's Bedrooms to ensure there is something to suit all customers; having a range of products will help to broaden the target market and attract different customers.

12 All businesses need to regularly review their marketing mix to check it is effective. Many issues – such as social, economic and technological changes – can mean that it needs adapting. This means reviewing all four aspects – Product, Price, Place and Promotion. Steven needs to do this to identify changes that he could make to attract younger customers.

He should review his product range and find out the type of furniture that young people want to buy and can afford. It may be that they prefer to buy flat pack furniture which they can put up themselves to save money. Or Steven could offer a budget range that is specially designed and includes a desk and an area for a laptop or for a TV. He could carry out research to find out what his new target market likes to buy.

He should review his prices to check what these customers can afford to pay and how they like to pay, for example he should accept credit cards because young buyers may not have the cash to pay the full price immediately. He needs to identify his main competitors and find out what they offer and how much they charge.

He should check that his website is modern and attractive and is highly placed on Google so that it is on the first page when people search for bedroom furniture in his area. He should investigate the potential for ecommerce and see how this would benefit his business. He may be able to sell some bedroom items online or give quotes if people contact him with their room measurements. He should also have a mobile site so that people can view his site from their smartphones. He needs to make it easier for people to find out about his product range and prices online rather than just visiting the showroom.

Steven should start using social media. He could post films of fitted bedrooms on YouTube and include links to these. He could put different eye-catching designs on the vans so that people would notice them and take photos and share these online. He could post pictures of new designs and ask people to 'like' and 'share' them. The more he can take advantage of viral marketing opportunities, the more his brand will get known to his target market.

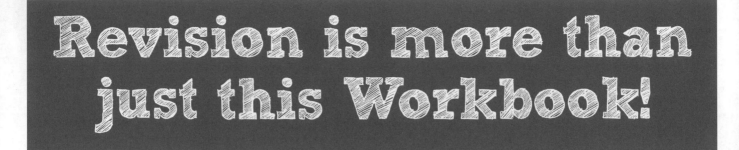

Revision is more than just this Workbook!

You'll need plenty of practice on each topic you revise

One topic per page for hassle-free revision!

1-to-1 page match with this Revision Workbook.

Detailed 'worked examples' help you get started on questions.

Written with learners in mind.

Content broken down into easily digestible points.

'Now try this' questions launch you into your Revision Workbook practice...

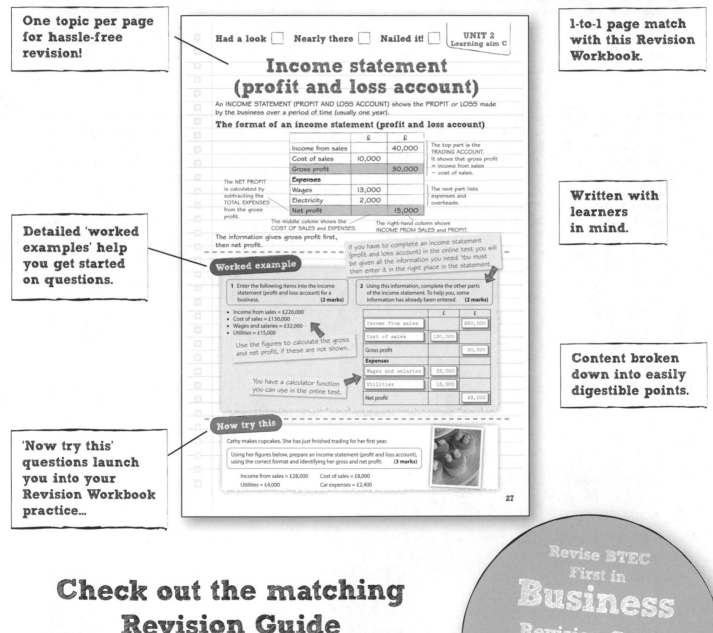

Check out the matching Revision Guide